P9-DEC-506

Religion *and* Nursing

Samuel Southard

RELIGION *and* NURSING

BROADMAN PRESS
Nashville, Tennessee

Fourth Printing

422-083

Library of Congress catalog card number 59-9773

Printed in the United States of America

1.5S68KSP

To My Mother

STELLA MILLER SOUTHARD

a graduate of the Winston-Salem
General Hospital School of Nursing, 1912
a Red Cross Nurse, World War I

Contents

Religion *and* Nursing

Introduction

NURSES ASK TWO KINDS OF QUESTIONS about religion. The first is about the relation of religion to their own lives and might be illustrated with the question of one student nurse: "What will sustain us all through our nurses' preparation and positions later on?" The second type of question concerns patients' religion. One student inquired: "Do patients expect a nurse to be interested in their spiritual life, or do they just consider her 'nosy' if she asks about it?"

This book has been written with both of these inquiries in mind. One purpose of the text is to lead the nurse toward sources of spiritual strength which will sustain her as she prepares for and pursues an exacting and challenging career. The second purpose is to relate religious resources to the nurse's work with patients.

Before an author can offer help he must know what the problems are. In 1956 student nurses in a number of denominational and nondenominational hospitals were asked: "What five questions about religion would you like to have answered in a textbook on religion and nursing?" Two thousand questions were received. A classification of them determined the outline and subject matter of this book. The author is especially indebted to Dr. Charles Bachmann for his compilation of questions from Protestant, Catholic, and Jewish student nurses in the Edward J. Meyer Memorial Hospital, Buffalo, New York.

In a text for nurses the problems must be seen from the nurses' point of view. To maintain this focus the verbatim interviews in this book were drawn from those submitted by student nurses. They are disguised so that there is no reference to any individual, living or dead. However, if a nurse sees herself in any illustration, let her look carefully at her own conscience. These examples are true to life.

Since the author is a clergyman, he does not presume to speak of detailed professional problems in the field of nursing ethics. Textbooks on nursing ethics have been available for many years and may be found in any nursing school library.

The author is also limited by his own religious viewpoint. He is writing as a Protestant. Nurses who are interested in a Catholic orientation may consult such authors as Fathers Edwin F. Healy, Charles McFaddin, John P. Kenny, and Joseph B. McAllister. The limited information in the text about Catholic and Jewish people is not intended to teach the nature of these religions.

The need for a Protestant text in religion and nursing has increased as schools of nursing have added lectures or courses on religion or the Bible and nursing. Such courses have been offered for many years in denominational hospitals. Since many Southern Baptist schools require such a course, the author was asked by the Southern Baptist Chaplains' Association to prepare a text on "The Bible and Nursing." The Association encouraged the author, read and criticized the original manuscript, and paid for the expense of mimeographing and mailing the text to the fifty or more chaplains in the Association. The manuscript was also read and criticized by thirty chaplains of other denominations in the American Protestant Hospital Association. Chaplain Carl Scherzer, Protestant Deaconess Hospital, Evansville, Indiana, was especially helpful.

Sixteen nursing educators, administrators, and authors provided mature and exact comments on the text. The author was able to obtain an interfaith evaluation through the kindness of Kathleen Black, director of the Mental Health and Psychiatric Nursing Service of the National League for Nursing; Olga Weiss, associate editor of *Nursing Outlook;* Rabbi David Seligson, Central Synagogue, New York; and Margaret Foley, Division of Nursing Education, Catholic Hospital Association. Other readers were: Frances Brush, Methodist Hospital, Houston; Mary Frey, Augustana Hospital, Chicago; Carola Haaland, National Lutheran Nurses Guild; Julia Kasmeier, Board of Nurse Examiners for the State of Texas; Fredericka Koch and the staff of the School of Nursing, Methodist Hospital, Indianapolis; Lillian Kuster, National Federation of Licensed Practical Nurses; Ruby Laeger, Hillcrest Medical Center, Tulsa; Ann Neil, Ogbomosho, Nigeria, Africa; Susie Cripe, Religious Life Committee, Presbyterian–St. Luke's Hospital, Chicago; Mildred Schier, Department of Diploma and Associate Degree Programs, National League for Nursing; Mrs. Virginia Stinert, Enid General Hospital; Marie Terbeck, Lutheran Hospital, Cleveland; and Dean Marjorie Bartholf, University of Texas, Galveston.

The biblical and theological material was checked by Professor Earl Joiner, Stetson University; Professor Ted Clark, New Orleans Baptist Seminary; and professors W. W. Adams and Tom Hall of the Southern Baptist Seminary.

The text was read from a doctor's point of view by Dr. Hamilton McKay, former president of the Southern Medical Association; Dean Stanley Olsen, Baylor University College of Medicine; Dr. J. W. Dorman, Baltimore; Dr. Wyatt Norvell, New Castle, Kentucky; and Dr. William Miner, former president of the Southeastern Section, American Urological Association. The chapters on ethics have been read from a lawyer's point of view by Cecil N. Cook of Houston, Texas.

The mimeographing and distribution of the manuscript would not have been possible without the assistance of the Institute of Religion, Texas Medical Center, Houston. The director of the Institute, Dr. Dawson C. Bryan, was a constant source of encouragement to the author when he was professor of pastoral care in the Institute.

Suggestions for Teaching

The material in this text was first presented in a seminar for nursing supervisors and head nurses of the Methodist Hospital, Houston, in co-operation with Chaplain Elton Stephenson and Clyde Verheyden. The professors of the Institute of Religion then used it in the schools of nursing of the Methodist, Memorial, and Hermann hospitals of Houston. From these lectures the text was prepared and distributed for teaching to chaplains Joe Luck and Bob Wimp of Memorial Hospital; Chaplain Charles Myers, Hendrix Memorial Hospital; and Frances Nicoll, Baptist Student Union Secretary, North Carolina Baptist Hospital.

The author collaborated with chaplains Luck and Wimp in a three-year program of teaching at Memorial Hospital. Out of this experience the following suggestions are made:

(1) Chapters 1–10 may be taught to first-year student nurses in weekly lectures. For schools of nursing which require a course in Bible, the first two chapters provide an outline and bibliographical references.

(2) The chapters on ethics (11–12) are designed for seminars with student nurses during their training in obstetrical, gynecological, and pediatric nursing.

(3) The chapter on religion and psychiatry (13) should be discussed in ward conferences with students during their training in psychiatric nursing.

(4) The lectures on the first ten chapters and the ethics and psychiatric seminars may be presented by a professional chaplain. Students are more free in the lecture discussion period if nursing instructors are not present. This latter observation also seems to be true of the seminars on ethics. The psychiatric seminar should be attended by nursing instructors or supervisors so that the students' impressions and opinions may be checked by the graduate nurses' knowledge of personnel and patients who are being discussed.

Finally, this word to both students and teachers: It is easy to oversimplify the problems of the sick. Ultimately, men are dependent upon the redemptive grace of God for healing. This great and wonderful mystery is not always clear to human eyes. The following pages, therefore, will not supply all the "answers." It is hoped that this book will help nurses and others to understand the spiritual problems of illness and to become channels through which the grace of God may work.

I. The Bible and Nursing

IF A NURSE WISHES to know about religion, she must begin by knowing something about the Bible because the Bible gives witness to the things which God has done and is doing for mankind. It not only contains evidence concerning the ways in which God spoke to the prophets and then in full measure through Jesus Christ, but it is also a living Word. It speaks boldly, proclaiming that through it men may be led to life in Christ.[1]

This is the reason why the Bible is the first topic of discussion in this course on the nurse and her religion. This book provides first-hand witness concerning God. However, the final and complete message of God has been spoken through a Person rather than a book—that is, through Jesus Christ. The Christian believes in a historical Christ, and this in turn means that there must be a record to provide a concise and clear picture of him.

The Christian can be specific about his faith because God has been specific. God's loving act in revealing himself through Jesus Christ is unique, final, adequate, and indispensable for salvation.[2] This is not an individual view; it is a statement of what has been believed by Christians since the days when Jesus walked the earth. Whether a nurse believes this herself or not, it is of the utmost importance that she recognize the fact that most of the patients who call themselves Christians do believe it.

---

[1] John 20:31. Biblical quotations in this book are from the Revised Standard Version unless otherwise noted.

[2] Acts 4:12; John 3:16; 2 Cor. 5:19.

In this book differences in Christian beliefs will be noted, such as varying interpretations of the Bible or Roman Catholic and Protestant views on birth control. Whenever a Jewish practice differs from those of Christians, this also will be mentioned.

How God Makes Himself Known

The Christian believes that God makes himself known to man. He reveals himself through nature, history, and human personality.

God revealed in nature.—To look through a binocular microscope at the intricate connections of vessels in the liver, lung, or kidney is an opportunity to marvel at God's handiwork. The careful study of an embryo from blastula to full-term fetus is an awesome revelation of the unfolding purposes of God in human creation. In her study of natural science, a nurse has many occasions to exclaim with the psalmist, "O Lord, how manifold are thy works! In wisdom hast thou made them all." [3]

The ancient Hebrews also looked upon the varied life of nature and found in it a unity that encouraged their dependence on God. Divine activity was seen in the creation of the world, in the continued growth of nature, and in its transformation of nature to serve the purposes of God.[4] When God spoke, it was with the authority of the Creator: "For thus says the Lord, who created the heavens (he is God!), who formed the earth and made it . . . 'I am the Lord, and there is no other.' " [5] Men wonder that God should be mindful of them when he has spread his majesty through the glorious heavens.[6]

God was and is continually at work in his creation. The process of fetal development led the psalmist to praise God, "For thou didst form my inward parts, thou didst knit me together in my mother's womb. I praise thee, for thou art fearful and wonderful." [7] All nature continues by the activity of God.

---

[3] Psalm 104:24.

[4] H. Wheeler Robinson, *Inspiration and Revelation in the Old Testament* (Oxford: Clarendon Press, 1945), pp. 17 ff.

[5] Isa. 45:18. [6] Psalm 8.

[7] Psalm 139:13–14.

When he takes away the breath of created things, they die and return to dust.[8]

Not only is God active in the world that he has created, but he also transforms nature. It is in relation to God's transforming activity that we should look at *miracles*. Because nature and human history are a part of the continued activity of God, Christians can accept such miracles as the crossing of the Red Sea and Jesus' healing of lepers as signs of divine concern for men.

Many modern difficulties concerning miracles arise from a distorted picture of God's activity in the world. Since the eighteenth century many people have thought of God as a cosmic watchmaker who created the world, wound it up, and then left it to tick for itself forever. But the biblical writers considered God's continued power to be indispensable for the daily working of this world. They believed that a God who was so intimately concerned with his world could certainly use his creation as an instrument of self-revelation. Jesus healed a blind man "that the works of God might be made manifest in him."[9]

Also, modern scientists are not as dogmatic about fixed natural laws as they were two hundred years ago. They now think of a fluid, expanding universe rather than a closed system of interlocking laws. Many possibilities are recognized today, including the probability that a force greater than man is operating in the world in a way that is only dimly comprehended by men.[10]

What has just been said about the close relationship between God and nature does not mean that the Hebrews worshiped nature. Rather, they believed that God was the Lord of nature and used nature as one method of revealing himself. The merely physical event of a miracle was not enough in itself. A human interpreter was required. Unbelieving men might see a miracle of God and still ignore their Creator. As Jesus said in the para-

---

[8] Psalm 104:29. [9] John 9:3.

[10] For further reading see *Modern Science and Christian Faith* (Wheaton, Ill: Van Kampen Press, 1956); D. S. Cairns, *The Faith That Rebels* (New York: Harper & Brothers, 1954); Charles E. Raven, *Christianity and Science* (New York: Association Press, 1955); and Sir Arthur Eddington, *The Nature of the Physical World* (New York: The Macmillan Company, 1928), p. 338.

ble of the rich man and Lazarus, some would not believe though one were raised from the dead.[11]

God revealed in history.—God's great acts in history were interpreted by prophets. Before these men are considered, it is important to study the great events which they clarified.

In the Old Testament the deliverance from Egypt was the great event of which the Hebrews were continually reminded. Here again an interpreter was required. God explained the significance of the deliverance from Egypt to Moses: "And I have come down to deliver them out of the hand of the Egyptians, and to bring them up out of that land to a good and broad land . . . the cry of the people of Israel has come to me, and I have seen the oppression with which the Egyptians oppress them." [12] God's personal concern for his people stood behind the miracles in Egypt and the crossing of the Red Sea. To the Egyptians it meant nothing but suffering and caused them further to harden their hearts.

In the New Testament the central event was the coming of God in the person of his Son, Jesus Christ. The early Christian church preached with conviction that God's saving activity in the past was a preparation for the final revelation of himself in Christ. The faith of Abraham, the escape from Egypt, and the law of Moses, as well as the words of the prophets in a time of national disaster, were a part of God's great plan to save men.[13]

The important word to emphasize in this connection is "saving" history. Just as God revealed his care for people through nature, so he revealed himself through great acts in history. Although both nature and history are under the control of God, certain natural occurrences and specific historical occasions became the special instruments with which God declares himself.

The nurse probably has more opportunity than most young women to observe God at work through specific events. Here, for example, is a conversation between a student nurse and a patient who was recovering from major surgery:

---

[11] Luke 16:31. [12] Ex. 3:8–9.
[13] Acts 7:1–54; Heb. 1:1–4; 11:1–40.

NURSE: Good morning, Mr. Johnson. I am glad to know that you rested better last night.

MR. JOHNSON: I feel so much better. I feel better inside, too.

NURSE: Better inside?

MR. JOHNSON: Well, you know how serious this kind of operation is. I just got to feeling yesterday that I owed a great deal to God for having brought me through this. It kind of upset me.

NURSE: The fact that God brought you through this crisis,—this was upsetting to you?

MR. JOHNSON: Uh—well, when the stakes are high, you think about your life more than—well, at least more than I had thought about things that were worthwhile for many years. I didn't make any big promises to God before the operation—that always seemed like bribery to me—but I had a feeling deep inside me that I would take more time for my wife and kids, and some other things, if I came through this.

NURSE: It sounds like you've done some mighty important thinking, Mr. Johnson.

MR. JOHNSON: Yeah, a feeling of—well, gratitude. I haven't felt that way in years.

In a historical event, an operation, Mr. Johnson came face to face with the issues of life and death which had been submerged in the rush of his successful business career. He saw the renewed significance of his family. After the operation a refreshing, long-delayed feeling of gratitude swept over him.

God revealed through personality.—But why is it that some people's spirits are mellowed by illness while others become more difficult to live with? Obviously there is something within man which causes him to interpret events in a certain way. It is his individual outlook that makes the difference. This distinguishes him as a personality. Human personality is the third great source through which God makes himself known to men.

When he thinks of God revealing himself in a Person, the Christian immediately thinks of Christ, for he was God's full revelation in human form. In the days of old God spoke through the prophets, but in the fullness of time he spoke through his son.[14] Christianity is a personal religion. The people of the Bible

---

[14] Heb. 1:1–3.

had wills of their own and were subject to all the pitfalls and mistakes of humanity. The Lord spoke to Abraham, who was afraid to acknowledge that Sarah was his wife; to Moses, who in righteous anger killed an Egyptian; to David, who committed adultery; to Elijah, who thought he was the only servant of God in all Israel. At only one time did he speak through a perfect personality, Jesus Christ, and even the Saviour of mankind accepted human limitations for his earthly life and suffered temptation, agony, and crucifixion.[15]

The disclosure of God in the Person of Jesus Christ is the basis for the doctrine of the Incarnation. Jesus stated this doctrine very simply when he said to Philip, "He who has seen me has seen the Father." [16] A nurse caught this same thought when she was teaching Sunday school class for the children in the pediatric department. A five-year-old boy asked her what God was like. She thought for a few seconds and then said, "God is like Jesus."

There will be many occasions when the nurse will be helped by the knowledge that God works through human personality. For example, a "high-strung" woman who entered the hospital because of sleeplessness and loss of weight asked the nurse:

PATIENT: Do you think it is ever right to talk to somebody about a private matter?

NURSE: You would like to talk to someone?

PATIENT: Well, I wonder if it is right to speak about something that I have been forbidden to talk about.

NURSE: It sounds as though it's troubling you a good deal—

PATIENT: Well, yes, but my husband says that we should just talk it over with God alone.

NURSE: I was reading in the Bible the other night that God sent a man to Paul in Damascus to open Paul's eyes. I believe that God wants us to share our troubles with someone. I wonder if you have thought of talking this over with your doctor or with our chaplain?

Perhaps the husband was trying to use religion to keep the wife away from other people. Yet she felt an overwhelming need to share her burden with a sympathetic person. The Bible contains

---

[15] Phil. 2; Heb. 4:14–16.

[16] John 14:9.

many examples of men who found God through inspired persons. God used such persons to make his will known. Paul presented the importance of a human mediator in these questions: "But how are men to call upon him in whom they have not believed? And how are they to believe in him of whom they have never heard? And how are they to hear without a preacher? And how can men preach unless they are sent?" [17]

The Christian believes that God has made himself known through reliable witnesses in the world, the great events of history, and Christ. Each of these can make a personal impression upon people today.

How God Makes Himself Known in the Bible

It is in terms of inspired personalities that the inspiration of Scripture can best be described. The divine revelation has come through human relationships. The Scriptures were written by human hands; even the most conservative Christian scholars do not maintain that the Bible is a perfect reproduction of God's handwriting.[18] The manuscripts have passed through many hands. The Bible also reflects human conditions. Each of the four Gospels, for example, was written for a different audience for a number of purposes. The Scriptures also transmit human ideas, for Paul admitted that he had no command from the Lord concerning an unmarried person and gave his own opinion on the subject.[19]

The fact that God spoke through human personality does not mean that the Bible is nothing more than a human interpretation of religious experience. Such a viewpoint would miss the evangelistic fervor of the Bible. It was God who did the speaking and man who answered. Like a voice out of a whirlwind, the Lord asked: "Who is this that darkens council by words without knowledge? Gird up your loins like a man, I will question you, and you shall declare to me." [20] In the Bible the conversation

---

[17] Rom. 10:14–15.

[18] Bernard Ramm, *Protestant Biblical Interpretation* (Boston: W. A. Wilde Co., 1950), p. 131.

[19] 1 Cor. 7:25.

[20] Job 38:2–3.

between God and man began with God. It was "the word of the Lord" that was spoken by his prophets.[21]

Some people will put the emphasis upon the progressive response of man rather than upon the primary questions of God. This emphasis was very well received in the influential writings of Dr. Julius Bewer [22] and Dr. Harry E. Fosdick.[23] The difficulty with this point of view was that too much emphasis was placed on personal interpretations of religious experience. The historical events were given less importance. These writers neglected the primary purpose of the biblical authors, which was to testify about what they had seen and heard.[24]

Other people put all the emphasis upon God's activity. A member of the editorial staff of the Scofield Bible wrote, "Therefore the words are inspired, or God breathed, including every inflection of the words, and every little particle." [25] There are three difficulties with this point of view. In the first place, a skeptic may find some contradictions in the Bible, such as the statement in 2 Samuel 24:1 that the Lord told David to take a census and the statement in 1 Chronicles 21:1 that Satan told him to do this. Thus if a Christian takes an all-or-nothing stand, the admission of any differences would destroy his entire belief in the divine inspiration of Scripture.

Second, such a view implies that every opinion expressed in the Bible is God's direct command. This does not help solve problems of interpretation such as the one which one nurse faced: "Are you to take everything in the Bible at face value—like the statement in 1 Corinthians 11 that women should not go to church with their heads uncovered—or take into consideration that this might just apply to a certain group of people in biblical times, not too much to us today?" A principle of interpretation which helps to answer this problem will be found on page 22.

---

[21] Hos. 1:1; Joel 1:1; Amos 2:1.

[22] *The Literature of the Old Testament* (New York: Columbia University Press, 1933).

[23] *A Guide to Understanding the Bible* (New York: Harper & Brothers, 1938).

[24] Luke 1:1–4; John 21:24; Gal. 1:11–12.

[25] William Pettingill, *Bible Questions Answered* (Findlay, Ohio: Dunham Publishing Co., n.d.), p. 8.

Third, a belief that every word of the Bible must be on the same level of inspiration ignores the obvious growth in the knowledge of God that is manifest in the Old and New Testaments. Elisha thought it right that King Jehu should destroy the whole house of Ahab because of Ahab's sin.[26] In those days the individual was so closely identified with the clan that the sin of one man was the sin of all. But at a later time God revealed to Hosea that this was wrong.[27] Jesus spoke of the gradual unfolding of God's truth when he told his disciples: "Truly I say to you, many prophets and righteous men longed to see what you see and did not see it and to hear what you hear and did not hear it." [28] The same truth is the theme of the book of Hebrews—that God's perfect revelation is Jesus Christ, who fulfills the imperfect religious system of the ancient Hebrews.

The inspiration of the Bible does not depend upon a judgment of the religious experience of the writers nor some theologian's theory of a special miraculous method of dictation. Belief rests upon the Bible's testimony to the individual heart of the great things that God has done.[29] This truth is more adequately expressed in the Westminster confession: "Our full persuasion and assurance of the infallible truth, and divine authority thereof [of the Bible], is from the inward work of the Holy Spirit, bearing witness by and with the word in our hearts." [30]

This great confession of the Reformation was built upon the doctrines of Luther and Calvin. Both of these men believed in the power of the Spirit of God to speak through the Scriptures to the minds of men. Luther believed: "The Scriptures, although they also were written by men, are not of men or from men, but from God." [31] In reply to the question of how he knew that this was God's word he answered, "You must determine this matter yourself, for your very life depends upon it. Therefore God

[26] 2 Kings 9:1–10; 10:11. [27] Hos. 1:4.

[28] Matt. 13:17.

[29] 1 John 1:1–3; Acts 5:32; John 20:31.

[30] Quoted in Alan Richardson, *A Preface to Bible Study* (London: Student Christian Movement Press, 1943), p. 19.

[31] Martin Luther, *Works of Martin Luther* (Philadelphia: Muhlenberg Press, 1915), II, 455.

must speak to your heart: this is God's word; otherwise you are undecided."[32] John Calvin taught that "the principal proof . . . of the Scriptures is everywhere derived from the character of the Divine Speaker. . . . It is necessary, therefore, that the same Spirit, Who spake by the mouths of the prophets, should penetrate into our hearts, to convince us that they faithfully delivered the oracles which were divinely entrusted to them."[33]

This emphasis upon the Holy Spirit as the guide is typically Protestant. The Roman Catholic nurse or patient would certainly accept the teaching that God speaks through the Bible but would not accept the freedom of interpretation which is implied in the statements of Luther and Calvin. Instead, the Roman Catholic believes that the Roman Catholic church is the "Mother of the New Testament" and that "if She had not declared the books composing the New Testament to be the inspired word of God, we would not know it."[34] The Roman Catholic would also interpret the Bible in harmony with the Roman Catholic system of doctrine, for if any meaning of a passage of Scripture is "not in harmony with the fact of inspiration and the spirit of the Church's interpretation [it] cannot be the true sense of Scripture."[35]

The nurse's religious conviction will therefore determine the way in which she will answer a question like, "How can we believe the Bible?" or, "How do we know the Bible speaks the truth?" The Protestant nurse will probably emphasize the testimony of the Holy Spirit to her own heart through the pages of the Bible, while the Roman Catholic nurse will probably emphasize the authority of her church.

God has made himself known in the Bible through the writings of inspired persons who interpreted the great acts of God in

---

[32] Quoted in Hugh Kerr, *A Compend of Luther's Theology* (Philadelphia: Westminster Press, 1943), p. 11.

[33] Quoted in Hugh Kerr, *A Compend of the Institutes of the Christian Religion* (Philadelphia: Presbyterian Board of Christian Education, 1939), p. 16.

[34] John A. O'Brien, *Finding Christ's Church* (Notre Dame, Ind.: Ave Maria Press, 1950), p. 21.

[35] A. J. Maaf, "Hermeneutics," *Catholic Encyclopedia*, VII, 272, quoted in Ramm, *op. cit.*, p. 26.

history. The purpose of these written words was to reveal the living Word, Jesus Christ.

Reading the Bible Today

If the purpose of the biblical writers was to make God known to the people of all ages, then a very pertinent question presents itself: "How are we to read the Bible as the word of God today?"

This is an important problem. The Bible speaks of events which happened two thousand or more years ago in a country where most of us have never lived. The words of the King James Bible are often quaint, misleading, or confusing. Even if the more accurate and clear Revised Standard Version is used, there are still such old-fashioned terms as predestination, regeneration, and covenant.[36]

Some writers have thought to answer this problem by condensing the Bible into a short form which contains the passages that are most easily understood by the modern reader. This is a good solution for children's Bible stories, but adults should not be treated like children. Other writers, like Thomas Jefferson, deliberately leave out sections of the Bible which are offensive to them. Mr. Jefferson did not believe in miracles, so he deleted all the miraculous stories of Jesus from the "Jefferson Bible." His edition of the Gospels closes with these words: "Now, in the place where He was crucified there was a garden and in the garden a new sepulchre wherein was never a man yet laid. There laid they Jesus, and rolled a great stone to the door of the sepulchre, and departed." [37] Thus he ignored the resurrection, the great event toward which the Gospels lead.

The early Christian church stood firm in its insistence that all of the Bible was to be accepted. When a wealthy shipowner, Marcion, began to teach in the second century that the Old

---

[36] Useful pamphlets to be used with the new RSV are: "Bible Words That Have Changed in Meaning," "An Introduction to the Revised Standard Version of the Old and New Testaments," "Understanding the Scriptures," and "The Living Word." All are published by Thomas Nelson & Sons, New York.

[37] Thomas Jefferson, *The Life and Morals of Jesus of Nazareth* (New York: Wilfred Funk, 1944), p. 132.

Testament and some of the books which later became the New Testament should be rejected, the church ejected him. He had made a gift of ten thousand dollars to charity when he joined the church. The church gave him back his money because it had condemned his teaching.

In those days Christians accepted the books of the Hebrew Bible as "the Scriptures." The divisions were as follows: the Law, or the Five Books of Moses; the Prophets; and the Writings.[38] During the first four centuries A.D., the Christian churches compiled an additional twenty-seven books which they called the New Testament. In addition, the Roman Catholic Church recognized the Apocrypha, a collection of Jewish writings which were presumably composed during the last two centuries before Christ. These books were included in a Greek translation of the Old Testament, called the Septuagint, which was used by some Christians and Jews in the first century A.D. At the Council of Jamnia, about A.D. 90, Jewish leaders fixed for all time the Hebrew text of their Bible, the Old Testament. The Apocrypha, "the hidden or spurious" books, which had not been widely accepted, were rejected.

Christians have taken different attitudes toward the Apocrypha. Roman Catholics include them in the Canon of Scriptures. Lutheran, Episcopalian, and Reformed churches believe they are edifying but not God's Word. The Apocrypha is rejected by other Protestant denominations which do not find in them the quality of inspiration that resides in the Old and New Testaments.[39]

The omission of the Apocrypha is one major difference between the Douay translation of the Bible used by Roman Catholics and the King James Version (A.D. 1611) used by Protestants. In addition, there are different translations of the same pas-

---

[38] A discussion of these books from a Jewish point of view may be found in S. B. Freehof, *Preface to Scripture* (Cincinnati: Hebrew Union College, 1950).

[39] For further reading see C. C. Torrey, *The Apocryphal Literature* (New Haven: Yale University Press, 1945); R. H. Pfeiffer, *History of New Testament Times, With an Introduction to the Apocrypha* (New York: Harper & Brothers, 1949); or his article in *The Interpreter's Bible* (New York: Abingdon-Cokesbury Press, 1952), I, 391–436.

sage. Thus the Douay version will say "do penance" while the King James will read "repent." Also, Protestant scholars may use newly discovered Greek or Hebrew manuscripts to correct earlier translations, whereas Roman Catholic scholars must remember that only the Latin translation of Jerome in the fourth century is authoritative for the Catholic.[40]

Although these matters are of interest to scholars, most nurses and their patients would find it difficult to distinguish a Roman Catholic from a Protestant translation of the Bible. Roman Catholics are encouraged to read any translation of the Bible which is approved by the bishop of their church. Protestant versions are not approved for Catholic reading.

The completeness of the Bible.—The Bible is considered a complete book. Christians insist on a study of both Old and New Testaments for several reasons.

First, the Bible gives the religious experience of a people over a period of fifteen hundred years. Unless both the Old and the New Testaments are read, the startling, revolutionary teachings of Jesus will not be appreciated. Jesus taught: "You have heard that it was said, 'You shall love your neighbor and hate your enemy.' But I say to you, 'Love your enemies and pray for those who persecute you.' "[41] The disciples had difficulty in accepting the application of these new truths. When James and John saw that certain Samaritans refused Jesus hospitality, they became angry and asked, "Lord, do you want us to bid fire come down from heaven and consume them?"[42] A thousand years before, Elijah had done the same thing.[43] But Jesus rebuked the disciples for their attitude. Only through knowledge of the Hebrew background of the disciples can we understand the reason for their question. If we cut out certain books of the Old Testament as "objectionable," the full significance of Jesus' teachings and actions would be lost to us.

Second, the Bible contains God's revelation to many different

---

[40] The literary supplement of the *London Times* for December 23, 1949, discusses the problem in its review of the new Knox (Catholic) translation of the Bible.

[41] Matt. 5:43–44.

[42] Luke 9:54.

[43] 2 Kings 1:1–16.

kinds of men, ranging from farmers to princes, during varying stages in world history. It is not a book like the Koran, which is the work of one man in one century. The warlike Song of Deborah in the early days of Israel's conquest (about 1300 B.C.), for instance, is in the same Bible with Isaiah's proclamation (about 700 B.C.) that in the last days the Lord shall judge between many nations: "They shall beat their swords into plowshares, and their spears into pruning hooks; nation shall not lift up sword against nation, neither shall they learn war any more." [44] Each piece of writing sparkles with a facet of God's truth. Alongside the sensuous raptures of the Song of Songs is the chaste description of courtship in the book of Ruth.[45] There is marital tragedy, such as the adultery of David [46] and the unfaithfulness of Hosea's wife. But there is also the joy of Mary that God should regard "the lowly estate of his handmaiden" and bless all generations through the fruit of her womb.[47]

Third, the biblical revelation contains all that is necessary to lead men to salvation and to a new way of life. Because Christianity is a historical religion, the early church believed those writings to be holy which were written by men who were personally near Christ. That which gave evidence of first-hand contact with the Lord or his disciples was read from the pulpit in the ancient church. There have been many writings in the history of the Christian church that were inspired by God, but only those which bear direct witness to Jesus in the days of his flesh are in the New Testament.[48]

Principles of interpretation.—To read the Bible is to be challenged with the question, "What will you do with Jesus?" If it were only literature or an interesting example of the development of religion among primitive people, it could be read and laid aside. But in the Bible God speaks to conditions in our age.

(1) In the Bible God speaks primarily through specific his-

---

[44] Isa. 2:4.

[45] Ruth 3:1–18.

[46] 2 Sam. 11 to 12:25.

[47] Luke 1:46–55.

[48] An authoritative answer to the question, *Which Books Belong in the Bible?* has been prepared by Professor Floyd W. Filson (Philadelphia: Westminster Press, 1957). See also the article on the formation of the Old and New Testaments in *The Interpreter's Bible,* I, 32–83.

torical events and inspired personalities. Therefore, the nurse need not look for some hidden meaning behind the description of what occurred in the deliverance of Israel from Egypt or the life of Jesus Christ. Concentration upon what the inspired writer actually says is the first principle of interpretation.

This may sound obvious to nurses, who are trained to observe symptoms closely and draw conclusions from such study. But throughout the ages many people have found comfort or inspiration by reading their own meanings *into* the Bible. Sometimes a meaning is drawn from Scripture which is different from the plain, literal intent. This is allegorical interpretation. Clement of Alexandria (*ca.* A.D. 190–202) typified this method. The story of the prodigal son, which is found in the fifteenth chapter of Luke, was interpreted by Clement in this way. He believed that the robe for which the father called when the son returned represented immortality; the shoes signified the upward progress of the soul; and Christ was symbolized in the fatted calf. Although this method of interpretation was repudiated by both the Roman Catholic scholars such as Thomas Aquinas and the Protestants like Luther and Calvin, it may still be found in late nineteenth century works such as the Scofield Bible.

(2) A second principle of interpretation is based on the unity of the Scriptures. As has already been said, God makes himself known by a combination of two unique features: prophetic personalities and the great events of history. No one person or event will be exactly like the others, but all of them share a revelation from one God. For example, a study of the method of conversion in the New Testament shows that Paul had a sudden, blinding experience with Jesus.[49] In contrast, the apostle John learned to know Jesus as the Christ gradually and followed him quietly.[50] In addition, there is no specific mention of a time when Timothy became a Christian.[51] The processes of conversion were different, but all had one thing in common—the experience of the saving grace of Christ.

This principle is often seen in nursing. A patient may say to a

[49] Acts 9:1–9.
[50] John 1:24–39.
[51] 2 Tim. 1:5.

nurse, "I joined the church when I was a child, but it's only been in these past few years that I have really felt close to God." The nurse may ask the patient what experiences brought this closeness to God. Through such a discussion both of them may share the Christian faith, although the nurse may have experienced a sudden change in her life at a definite date while the patient had a gradual spiritual awakening.

Amid the rich variety of religious experiences recorded in the Bible there are several great unifying ideas, such as the character of the holy and loving God, his covenant with those who believe in his faithfulness, the necessity of personal repentance, and the fellowship of believers in a chosen people or a church. Each of these great themes is the subject of many theological studies. For the nurse who is challenged to read more I would suggest three series of short and inexpensive books. One is the Layman's Theological Library, published by Westminster Press, Witherspoon Building, Philadelphia 7, Pennsylvania. Some of the books in this series are *A Faith for the Nations* by Charles Forman, which compares Christianity with other religions, and *Understanding the Bible* by Fred Denbeaux. The second, World Christian Books, published by Association Press, 291 Broadway, New York 7, New York, contains volumes such as the following: *John's Witness to Jesus* by George Appleton and *Who Is Jesus Christ?* by Stephen C. Neill. A third group, Apex Books, contains inexpensive editions of such outstanding works as *The Kingdom of God* by John Bright. These are published by Abingdon Press, Nashville, Tennessee.

(3) A third principle which the nurse should bear in mind is the distinction between literal prophecy and symbolic imagery. The statement in the first chapter of Acts that Jesus would return to earth is a literal prophecy. This may be taken literally because the return of Christ is a central belief of Christians and also because the book of Acts is primarily a factual, descriptive work with no allegory. By way of contrast, there is the vivid symbolism of the fourth through the twenty-second chapters of the book of Revelation. In these writings John sought to encourage the suffering church, but he had to disguise his language

lest the authorities find that he was speaking of Christ's triumph over Rome. It is futile to identify such an obscure figure as the beast or the dragon of Revelation 13 with some modern historical figure like the Kaiser or Hitler or Stalin. Nurses should not be disturbed by persons who use the obscure passages in Revelation to foretell things that are known only to God.[52] This has been done in every age, and history discredits such use of the symbolism in the book of Revelation.

(4) What has just been said about literal and symbolic prophecy implies a fourth principle of interpretation, which is that the reader must know something about the historical setting of a book and the personal background of its author. The author of the book of Revelation was writing to churches suffering under Roman persecution. They needed strength and encouragement. The book proclaims that Christ will be victorious over all evil and the suffering saints will be vindicated. If a nurse reads the book with this theme in her mind, she may think of ways in which its message gives comfort and courage in times of stress today. Unless she knows the historical setting and purpose of the writing, she may be perplexed by its unusual imagery or speculate unprofitably about the meaning of an obscure symbol.[53]

(5) A similar principle is to know the audience for whom the work was intended. The first letter of John was written in another time of crisis for the church. Christianity was beginning to reach men who had studied Greek philosophy. These men believed that it was philosophically impossible for God to come to earth as a man. People who wanted to be intellectual were afraid of being "unphilosophical" as they are of being "unscientific" in the twentieth century. The first letter of John was written to combat this charge. This is why this epistle emphasizes that Jesus was God in the flesh.[54]

If the personality of the writer as well as his religious experience, his audience, and the conditions under which he lived is

---

[52] Acts 1:7.

[53] See H. H. Rowley, *The Relevance of Apocalyptic* (New York: Harper & Brothers, 1955).

[54] 1 John 4:2–3.

known, the specific purpose of his writing will be more easily understood. For example, we may wonder why Matthew continually referred to the Old Testament unless we know that the Christian church accepted the Old Testament as divinely inspired and believed that Christ was the fulfilment of Old Testament prophecy. Matthew was probably writing for a group of Jewish Christians in Jerusalem who understood these things.

(6) The Bible is a guidebook rather than a rulebook. When isolated biblical passages are used as fixed rules, difficulties may arise such as those mentioned by the nurse who asked, "How is one to know whether to wear a hat in church or not, or to cut her hair or to wear jewelry?" Again, if all Scripture is equal, the question of whether to obey the Old Testament command to retaliate or the New Testament law to love your enemies arises. Obviously, the nurse must decide which commands are most important for her. How is she to decide?

First, for Christians, the Old Testament code does not govern the New Testament church. Christ's command to love our enemies is preferred over the "eye for an eye" doctrine of the Old Testament because Christ's life fulfilled the law. Faith in him now provides all the righteousness for which men strive.

Second, within the New Testament writings the teachings of Christ are of highest importance. No words of Jesus concerning the wearing of jewelry or the cutting of hair are recorded. We do have his command to cleanse "the inside of the cup and of the plate, that the outside also may be clean." [55] Therefore, if a person considers 1 Peter 3:3 and 1 Corinthians 11:5 as literal commands to be obeyed by all and if a person looks upon these outward signs as evidence of spirituality, the sense of Peter's statement is missed and the reader comes under the judgment of Jesus, as quoted above.

Third, a writer should be interpreted as consistent with himself. One student nurse was disappointed because she found no boy friend either in her church or among the medical students. She was embarrassed because she had boasted at home that she

---

[55] Matt. 23:26.

would marry an educated man rather than one of the "farm boys." Paul's words in 1 Corinthians 7:32–35 became her face-saver. She spoke of dedicating her life as a missionary nurse and laying aside bright prospects of marriage in order to "serve the Lord better." It was obvious to most of her friends that she was quite unhappy. Less friendly nurses thought she was a religious fanatic. Fortunately, she met an older, unmarried woman in religious work who helped her to see that work and friends can make life as satisfying, if not more so, than just getting married. This older friend also gave her the apostle Paul's positive interpretation of marriage as a state of being in which two people become one in love.[56] For the sake of wounded pride, the student nurse had used one statement by Paul and neglected those which would have corrected her attitude.

(7) A final general principle is related to the emphasis upon the meaning of the Bible for today. This principle is the question, "How does the experience of these inspired writers relate to my life?" A student nurse asked a hospital chaplain for help because of her trouble with a boy friend. "My fiance can never make up his mind about me," she said. "He keeps comparing me unfavorably to his mother. He tells me how gracious and charming she is with people, how she can cook and sew. What can I do?" The chaplain asked her, "Do you want to be like his mother?" The nurse replied that she didn't, for she had observed that when her fiance was with his mother, he was sarcastic and irritable. "He always talks about how independent he is, but he ends up doing what she expects of him. But he's such a fine Christian around everyone else—except her and me. I don't understand it." The chaplain reminded her of Jesus's teaching that a man must leave his father and mother in order that he might cleave to his wife.[57] He asked her if she had discussed with her boy friend the fact that marriage implies a psychological leaving of parents so that the man and wife may "cleave" to each other and become one flesh.

After several conferences the nurse said, "You know, I have

---

[56] Eph. 5:21–23; 1 Cor. 7:1–7.

[57] Matt. 19:4–6.

been so upset about all this that I started to go back to my grandmother last week end. She's the one in the family that I have always been closest to. But I decided that it was time for me to learn some independence, too. This is the first time that I have not run straight to her with a problem, and I feel proud of myself."

In this example, the young lady had not only seen the application of a biblical passage to her boy friend but had also realized something of its meaning for her own life. Those who try out the experiences of the Bible in their own lives will find both power and wisdom from God.[58]

Resources for Bible study.—A nurse who has read the last section seriously will know that she cannot adequately interpret the Bible on the basis of these few basic principles. She must have additional help.

(1) *Interpretation.*—A simple introduction to Bible study is *How to Study and Use the Bible* by Park Hayes Miller.[59] Detailed principles of interpretation may be found in a book by H. E. Dana, *Searching the Scriptures.*[60] Robert M. Grant has written an interesting history of the different ways in which the Bible has been interpreted in *The Bible in the Church.*[61]

For those who have never read the Bible, one of the best books available is *Reading the Bible,*[62] written by a missionary, Daniel T. Niles. Although the book is a small one, it is full of meaning.

Many patients' questions about the Bible are related to common problems. *Getting Help from the Bible*[63] by Charles M. Crowe is designed to bring help from the Bible to people with everyday problems. It contains chapters entitled "Inner Quietness," "When Life Gets Ordinary," and "When We Are Sick in Mind and Body."

Another book organized around current questions is *The Bible Speaks to You.*[64] The author, Robert M. Brown, discusses

[58] 1 Cor. 1:18–31.
[59] New York: Association Press, 1955.
[60] Kansas City: Central Seminary Press, 1946.
[61] New York: The Macmillan Company, 1948.
[62] New York: Association Press, 1955.
[63] New York: Harper & Brothers, 1957.
[64] Philadelphia: Westminster Press, 1955.

biblical answers to problems like predestination, the miracles, the importance of Jesus, and the origin of the Bible. *Great Ideas of the Bible* [65] contains the Moffatt translation of Scripture passages which speak on such theological issues as suffering, faith, prayer, heaven, eternal life, human destiny, and the nature of God. Jewish students will be particularly interested in *Pathways Through the Bible* by Mortimer Cohen.[66]

(2) *Translations.*—For patients, the magazine-size editions of the Gospels and Acts are excellent. These contain the text in the plain English of the Revised Standard Version, surrounded by photographs and pictures which illustrate the geography, customs, and peoples of biblical times. These are available in single books or as an entire New Testament from the American Bible Society, 450 Park Avenue, New York 27, New York.

The Revised Standard Version is the one used in most Protestant theological seminaries. It retains the stately and poetic quality of the King James Version and at the same time corrects the archaic and the inaccurate phrases of earlier translations. A colorful and thought-provoking translation of the New Testament has been made by J. B. Phillips.

(3) *Dictionaries.*—Several nurses asked questions about specific biblical words like "selah" or "covenant." The meaning of such words can be found in a Bible dictionary. *The Westminster Dictionary of the Bible* [67] or *Harper's Bible Dictionary* [68] will be especially good for locating persons and places. *A Theological Word Book of the Bible* [69] will give the nurse a well-organized discussion of meanings of important biblical words like *God*, *sin*, *predestination*, and *miracle*, with references to the places they are used in Scripture.

(4) *Atlas.*—Why is it that a poor, small country like Israel should be in the midst of so many conflicts among ancient world

---

[65] New York: Harper & Brothers, 1955.

[66] Philadelphia: Jewish Publication Society, 1946.

[67] John D. Davis; revised by Henry Gehman (Philadelphia: Westminster Press, 1944).

[68] Madeleine S. Miller and J. Lane Miller (New York: Harper & Brothers, 1952).

[69] Alan Richardson, ed. (New York: The Macmillan Company, 1953).

powers? It was because of her location on trade routes midway between Egypt and Mesopotamia. *The Westminster Historical Atlas to the Bible* [70] locates biblical places and discusses the history of the region. Not only will such a volume help the nurse in her own study, but it will also give her understanding of what some patients say. One student was puzzled by a Jehovah's Witness on her floor who told her of the "coming great battle of Armageddon." The student had never read of such a place in the newspapers. Armageddon is a valley in Palestine where two great trade routes cross. So many battles have been fought around the fortress, Megiddo, that it has become a biblical name for the last great battlefield of the world.[71]

A geography that reads like a novel is *The River Jordan* [72] by Nelson Glueck.

(5) *Commentaries.*—The preceding references will not answer questions about specific books like Genesis, Matthew, or Revelation. A commentary on one book will help fill this need. Since commentaries for all sixty-six books in the Bible cannot be listed, the nurse should ask her pastor or chaplain for specific references. She will find a very concise discussion of commentaries, dictionaries, and other biblical resources in *Tools for Bible Study* [73] by Baumer Kelly and Donald Miller.

A nurse who can be consistent in her Sunday school attendance or lesson study will find that in five years she will have surveyed major portions of the Bible. The International Sunday School lessons, supplemented by the weekly study guides of each denomination, will constantly increase her biblical understanding.

(6) *History.*—Many nurses sent in questions about the history of Israel, the period between the Old and the New Testaments, and the New Testament world. A standard text on these subjects is *Essentials of Bible History* [74] by Elmer Mould. Volume

---

[70] George Wright and Floyd Filson (Philadelphia: Westminster Press, 1956).
[71] Rev. 16:16; Judg. 5; 1 Sam. 31; 2 Kings 23.
[72] Philadelphia: Westminster Press, 1946.
[73] Richmond: John Knox Press, 1955.
[74] New York: Ronald Press, 1951.

one of a newer reference work, *The Interpreter's Bible*,[75] has some excellent articles on the history and religion of Israel. Volume seven contains articles of high quality on the world of the New Testament. *Ancient Israel*[76] by Harry Orlinsky of Hebrew Union College is a factual account of Israel's history from 2000 to 400 B.C.

Archeology has shed much light upon the history of Old and New Testament times. Jack Finegan's *Light from the Ancient Past*[77] gives this background of the Hebrew-Christian religion.

(7) *General reference.*—A number of specific subjects such as the history and contents of the Apocrypha, the meaning of biblical inspiration, or the relevance of the prophets for today are discussed in books like *A Preface to Bible Study*[78] by Alan Richardson; *The Relevance of the Bible*[79] by H. H. Rowley; *An Introduction to the Bible*[80] by Stanley Cook; or *The Bible Today*,[81] edited by C. H. Dodd.

Several nurses asked about the Dead Sea Scrolls. Milton Burrows has an excellent translation and discussion of their significance in *The Dead Sea Scrolls*.[82]

(8) *Formation of the Bible.*—Many nurses asked how the Bible came into its present form and organization. *How Our Bible Came to Us*[83] by H. G. G. Herklots is a compelling story of the versions of the Bible from the early English translation of Wycliffe to the latest biblical sensation, the Dead Sea Scrolls. Another well-written study is *The Ancestry of an English Bible*[84] by Ira Price. *Our English Bible in the Making*[85] by H. G. May concentrates on recent revisions and translations of the English Bible.

---

[75] New York: Abingdon-Cokesbury Press, 1952.
[76] Ithaca, New York: Cornell University Press, 1954.
[77] Princeton: Princeton University Press, 1946.
[78] London: Student Christian Movement Press, 1943.
[79] New York: The Macmillan Company, 1944.
[80] London: Penguin Books, 1945.
[81] New Cambridge, England: Cambridge University Press, 1947.
[82] New York: Viking Press, 1955.
[83] New York: Harper & Brothers, 1956.
[84] Philadelphia: Westminster Press, 1952.
[85] New York: Abingdon-Cokesbury Press, 1952.

Systematic study for Scripture reading.—In medical schools which followed the German tradition, students in pathology used to be handed a tray of slides and told to "look at them." But what student could memorize five thousand slides? In the same way, reading one book after another in the Bible without any organization would be confusing. Therefore, a text that will guide systematically through the Scripture is needed, for the Bible must be understood on its own terms before its full meaning for today can be known.

One of the most comprehensive texts is *The New Bible Handbook*, edited by G. T. Manley.[86] The first section of this work considers questions about the whole Bible, such as inspiration, authority, modern criticism, miracles, and principles of interpretation. Other sections give brief accounts of the authorship, date, and context of each book.

A two-volume work, *Understanding the Old Testament*[87] and *Understanding the New Testament*,[88] has been written for university students. These texts bring together many elements of Bible study: the development of Scripture, the historical background, and the theological truths revealed through the inspired writers. Their ideas will be in harmony with students who hold to a liberal theology. *The New Bible Handbook* is written from a more conservative point of view.

A general introduction to basic Christian belief, written for young people, is *Understanding Christianity*[89] by Edgar McKown and Carl Scherzer. If a nurse is interested in a discussion group on such questions as the use of the Bible, the Christian's idea of God, prayer, and the life to come, this book will provide much helpful material. One of the authors, Pastor Scherzer, is chaplain of the Protestant Deaconess Hospital, Evansville, Indiana.

---

[86] Chicago: Inter-Varsity Christian Fellowship, 1949.
[87] B. W. Anderson (Englewood Cliffs: Prentice-Hall, 1957).
[88] H. C. Kee and R. W. Young (Englewood Cliffs: Prentice-Hall, 1957).
[89] New York: Ronald Press, 1949.

2. Theology and Nursing

BIBLICAL RELIGION is always thought of as man's response to God's revelation. The ways in which God makes himself known and his specific self-disclosure in the Bible have already been discussed. The next step is to investigate more closely the God who is revealed in the Scriptures and relate this knowledge to the nurse's work with patients.

Who is God? From a nurse's point of view this is not just an abstract theological question. Patients often confront nurses with an opinion of God and ask the nurses' ideas. A first-year student gave an example of this in her own words:

> One of my patients was being divorced by his wife. They had a little girl about five years old. He stated that although he was much older than his wife, he gave her everything she wanted.
>
> He wanted to know what I thought of the whole matter. I told him I did not know. Later in the conversation I told him that maybe it was God's will for the divorce to go through. Since there was a chance they would separate later, maybe it was better that they do so now while the child was young.[1]
>
> Several times during our discussion he wanted me to agree with him that God would punish his wife for what she was doing. I didn't agree. He really believed that God would punish her.

A nurse who is spiritually sensitive to the needs of patients knows the importance of God's character. It *does* make a dif-

[1] The student does not really know enough about the patient's family to offer this opinion.

ference what a person believes. Christians were inspired by their faith in Jesus to overcome their own suffering and extend compassion to others in need. Since it was God's nature to love, they were commanded to show love by "deed and truth" to one another. One way to do this was through attention to the physically ill. "The Christian practice of collecting the sick and infirm in places where they could be ministered to was the beginning of the hospital as we know it." [2]

The God of Israel

Christians and Jews believe that God made himself known to Abraham, Moses, and the other prophets. As H. Norman Snaith argues so persuasively in *The Distinctive Ideas of the Old Testament*,[3] a comparison with other religions shows us the unique and distinctive quality of the Hebrews' God. This radical break of Israel with the gods of other people can be seen in the character of Jehovah. The following discussion owes much to G. Ernest Wright's presentation of Israel's God in *The Old Testament Against Its Environment*.[4] The purpose is to relate the Hebrew-Christian knowledge of God to the nurse's work with hospital patients.

Who is the God of Israel?

(1) First of all, the God of Israel is the Creator of the world. He was not created as were the divine rulers of the ancient Babylonians, who were formed from the bodies of still more ancient beings. Jehovah is the God of both the heaven and the earth. Thus he was known to the most ancient of the patriarchs, Abraham.[5]

This knowledge that God is more than nature gave strength to men in time of distress. When there was a physical catastrophe, it was not necessarily a sign of God's wrath. Instead, the psalmist could proclaim, "God is our refuge and strength, a very present help in trouble." [6] On one occasion a pastor read this verse to a

---

[2] R. B. Allen, *Medical Education and Changing Order* (New York: Commonwealth Fund, 1946), p. 10.

[3] Philadelphia: Westminster Press, 1946.

[4] London: Student Christian Movement Press, 1950, pp. 22–41.

[5] Gen. 24:3.

[6] Psalm 46:1.

woman whose husband had died suddenly. The man had been in what seemed to be good health that morning. In the afternoon she received a call that he had been taken to the hospital with a heart attack. He died within an hour after she arrived at his bedside. When the chaplain read "God is our refuge and strength . . . ," she said, "Oh, that is my favorite verse of Scripture." In her time of distress God was not thought of as the cause of her sorrow but as a source of comfort and security.

(2) Jehovah is the Lord of history. He brought the people of Israel out of Egypt and delivered Canaan into their hands. Centuries later the proud king of Assyria was but the "rod of my anger" against a spiritually corrupt Israel.[7] Human history is his constant concern.

God does actively care for his world, but it is difficult for some doctors, nurses, and patients to accept this truth. One doctor discovered it rather suddenly. With hardship and intense effort he worked his way through medical school and his internship. As a resident he would hardly allow an intern to get near one of his patients—he had to do everything himself. One of the pastors in the town where this doctor was located observed the ceaseless activity of this resident. They became good friends. Time and again the resident would explain that he could not meet his friend for dinner or a game of golf because he felt that he had to be close by his patients. Finally the pastor said, "You don't leave anything for God to do, do you?"

(3) The God of Israel is mysterious and holy. No image can be made of him.[8] Archeologists have found many Canaanite images of gods and goddesses, but they have never found an image of a male deity in an ancient Israelite town.[9] Biblical Hebrew has no word for goddess. The licentious fertility rites of the neighboring tribes were condemned, and the temple prostitutes of the Canaanites were abhorrent to the prophets of the Hebrews.

"To whom then will you liken God, or what likeness compare

[7] Isa. 10:5. [8] Ex. 24; Deut. 5:8.

[9] G. Ernest Wright, *The Old Testament Against Its Environment* (London: Student Christian Movement Press, 1950), p. 24.

with him?"[10] cried the prophet Isaiah. To make the Holy God after the image of man was considered to be idolatry.

Since few patients bring fetishes of wood or charmed stones into American hospitals, nurses may forget the significance of God's command that no image be made of him.[11] It has taken the insights of modern psychologists to point out a new psychological idolatry. Some people have raised up an "ideal image" of themselves and begun to worship it.

The symptoms of this idolatry may be seen in the following illustration. A woman with ill-defined symptoms of "heartburn" and "hot flashes" asked a nurse what time the chaplain usually came by. When the nurse said that he often came in the afternoon to this part of the hospital, the woman said, "I wish he could come early in the afternoon before my husband arrives." The nurse heard this reference to the husband and told the chaplain that there was probably something in the personal relationship of the husband and wife that would bear investigation. The chaplain came early in the afternoon and found it to be as the nurse had suspected. The woman was literally burning up with resentment toward her husband. She said that he was not a man, that he was lazy, that he did not do his share of the yard work, that he took out the children when she asked him to but never took her out. When the chaplain asked if she had told her husband these things, she said, "No, I just try to figure them out for myself. It would just lead to a disagreeable scene, and I don't want to be responsible for something like that. I should be able to work this problem out like I have worked others out, but I can't. What's wrong with me?"

Instead of trying an on-the-spot diagnosis, the chaplain helped

---

[10] Isa. 40:18.

[11] Some Protestant nurses may think of their Catholic patients' medals, rosaries, etc., as fetishes. It is true that some Catholics use them as objects of superstition, but Catholics are repeatedly warned against that attitude. These objects are not to be looked upon as having intrinsic power of their own but as material objects which may be used with the blessing of the Church as a stimulus to faith and fervor. A Catholic patient's medals may mean a great deal to him. Protestants will not agree with Catholics in the use of these objects, but if a Protestant nurse looks upon them as of no importance to the Catholic patient, she may disturb her patient and alienate herself from him.

her to understand her pattern of behavior by asking, "You mean you always try to figure things out without talking them over?" The woman said that it was so and gave many examples from her early life. Finally she said, "I had to use my wits when I was young to get what I wanted in a family of five boys. I have always been cool headed and objective. Why do I get so tense and nervous now?"

An unemotional, calculated approach to other people was the ideal which this woman had developed from childhood. But now she was confronted by the overwhelming emotions of rage and frustration against a husband whom she considered to be less than a man. She tried to throttle her feelings with her cool, dispassionate ideal. The repressed emotions then made themselves felt in bodily symptoms. The woman had erected an ideal that was not true to her deeper emotions.

Fortunately, this woman later learned to tell her husband some of her feelings. When that happened, he said in amazement, "Why, I never knew that you felt this way. You were always so self-sufficient. I always felt insignificant around you." When the husband began to see the womanly emotions of his wife, he was encouraged. But all this could not have taken place if an idol had not been smashed.

(4) God is personal. References to him are always in human terms. In Egyptian and Mesopotamian mythology the gods appear as birds, snakes, fish, or other animals. In the Bible, God's relation to man is spoken of in terms of human relationships, such as that of a father to his children: "As a father pities his children, so the Lord pities those who fear him." [12]

Sometimes a patient comes to a new understanding of God and of himself through speaking in terms of a human relationship. A nurse who was caring for several critically ill children heard snatches of a conversation between two of the fathers:

MR. ABERNATHY: I prayed a thousand times that my boy would get well, but the doctors give me no encouragement. Why doesn't God do something?

[12] Psalm 103:13.

MR. BROWN: Well, I figure that he has.

MR. ABERNATHY: Ha!

MR. BROWN: Oh, I used to feel that way when I first learned that my boy couldn't get well. It was a bitter experience. I couldn't bring myself to give up my son. But then I got to thinking of the fact that God gave up his Son for me. It made me feel that he understood what I'm going through now.

Mr. Brown had found spiritual strength through looking upon God as a Father who knows what it means to lose a son.

(5) Jehovah is the living God. He is not spiritually restricted to any one place or climate or kingdom. He is at home in heaven, the desert, or in the hearts of men.[13]

Some biblical characters found it difficult to accept these truths. Nathaniel had contempt for a little village like Nazareth: "Can anything good come out of Nazareth?" he asked when Philip told him that they had found Jesus.[14] But the Son of God came out of a village that Nathaniel despised. Peter thought that God belonged to the Jews. It took a vision from the Lord to show him that "God shows no partiality" among nations or races.[15]

Sometimes a student nurse loses sight of this truth. She may feel that God is not as close to her in the hospital as he is in a church or at home. But often there is a reminder that God is everywhere. One nurse found this truth in her ministry to an elderly woman.

It was the first Sunday morning I had had to miss church because I was on duty. For that reason I was depressed, and I must have carried some of my depression into my patient's room. My patient was a sweet little lady in her early eighties. During the course of the A.M. care she asked what church I attended. I replied, "Lutheran." "Do you attend regularly?" she then asked. "Yes ma'am, except for this morning since I had to work." "I think that's very nice. When we lived in St. Louis, some friends of ours were Lutheran and they used to take my little grandson to Sunday school every Sunday. Then we started going to the Baptist church regularly, and he went with us. We're

---

[13] Isa. 51:9–16.
[14] John 1:46.
[15] Acts 10:34.

Baptist, you know. Where is my Bible?" "I don't see one in here. Let me get one for you."

As I went to get the Bible for her, my cloud of depression began to lift. When I got back to her room and gave her the Bible, she said, "Before I got so sick I didn't ever miss church. But we can just read some passages from the Bible and say a prayer, and I think the Lord will accept that, don't you?" "Yes, ma'am, I think he will."

Just as it is difficult for some nurses to really feel that God is in the midst of a large, impersonal city, so it is hard for some patients to accept God's healing ministry through people of another color. A head nurse in a large Southern hospital asked the chaplain to visit a patient who was discourteous toward a Negro nurse on the night shift. The patient responded to the chaplain's conversation with these words:

Well, I have received good treatment here. You know, something happened last night. I've always used this hospital. But like a friend of mine said, "When I get sick, I want to look up and see a white face." I had a nigger wait on me, but she won't any more. (*long pause*) I can't help how I was brought up. You know the Bible says that color was put on Cain as a curse, doesn't it?

CHAPLAIN: Well, of course it does not say that the mark was blackness, and it was put on him for protection.

PATIENT: I hadn't thought of it that way. Anyway, it may seem strange I would say such a thing to you as a minister, but they have their place and should stay in it.

CHAPLAIN: Well, the best way to deal with a subject is to be honest about it. I can envision a society in which this wouldn't be a problem.

PATIENT: You can?

CHAPLAIN: Oh, I'm not saying that I have no prejudices. But I can recognize them as unchristian and seek to overcome them.

PATIENT (*after a pause*): I guess anyone in your profession would have to feel that way, wouldn't he?

CHAPLAIN: Well, my hope is that it is not primarily because of my profession but because of my Christianity that I feel that way.

PATIENT: Well, don't misunderstand me. I don't believe in abusing them. I was good to those cotton-field niggers on the farm. But here in the city they try to do white men's work . . .

The conversation continued in the same fashion, with the patient seeking to defend his feeling and the chaplain relating his feeling to Christianity. The chaplain missed a possible opportunity to relate the patient's concern to his insecure economic and social status. "Back home" he was at least better than "cotton-field niggers." But in the city he was forced to compete with people on a social level equal with himself and was beginning to doubt his own abilities. His earlier way of life was the only security he had known. It was comforting to identify God with it. But the Lord God is not that small.

(6) The God of Israel requires righteous living of his servants: "He has showed you, O man, what is good; and what does the Lord require of you but to do justice, and to love kindness, and to walk humbly with your God?" [16]

The tests of righteousness in a hospital are innumerable. Disease confronts men with ethical decisions. Nurses often remark that one patient "acts like a Christian" despite chronic pain while another patient is "using his handicap as a crutch." One student nurse was assigned to the latter type of person. The patient was a middle-aged man whose leg had been amputated six months previously. His physical complaints were ill-defined. The nurse noted his constant stream of demands upon his wife and teen-age daughter. When the chaplain visited the patient, the nurse invited the mother and daughter to see a TV program in the recreation room. This left the two men alone. The patient poured out a stream of bitterness: he could not work as much now, he was not respected by his family, his friends pitied him.

The chaplain left without much comment but returned on two occasions. On the third visit, the chaplain asked: "Have you decided to organize your life about a missing leg?" The patient replied in part: "I guess that's something I never thought about —maybe so. . . . Maybe I wanted to be treated differently. . . . Well, it doesn't make me feel good to say it, but I guess I've been using this crutch as a club to beat my wife into doing what I wanted her to do."

This patient had come face to face with what God required of him: love for his family and for himself despite a handicap. The

---

[16] Mic. 6:8.

chaplain's question helped the man to recognize his self-centeredness, bitterness, and coercion of others.

(7) "The Lord our God is one Lord."[17] He is the only God. To worship anything less is idolatry, sickness, and death. To organize life about a missing leg, a wounded ego, or chronic jealousy is to "go after other gods."

(8) Jehovah loves his people and shows his concern for them. "As a father pities his children, so the Lord pities those who fear him. For he knows our frame; he remembers that we are dust."[18]

Some people prefer to think of the Deity as an impersonal, immovable "it." But God is a "thou," the source of all human warmth, the model of all earthly affections. He loves men with an "everlasting love,"[19] like a father who yearns after a wayward son.[20] He is grieved because of man's sins, as a husband mourns a faithless wife.[21] His anger came upon his people because they spurned his love and deliberately despised the great commission which he gave.[22]

Many patients are comforted by the thought of God's personal concern for them. They are greatly relieved to know that the Holy One is revealed through emotions that are common to all men. One woman told her pastor how the strain of her husband's prolonged illness had brought her to the brink of madness. The pastor reminded her that Christians have a God who can sympathize with their weakness, because he has been tempted in all respects as they are.[23] This truth, given out of the understanding spirit of the minister, strengthened this woman in the knowledge that God really understood her condition. God knows what suffering is. The great Old Testament preface to the cross is found in the book of Isaiah, who spoke of One who will bear our griefs and carry our sorrows.[24]

The God of Israel is also the Father of our Lord Jesus Christ. Christians have always regarded the fifty-third and some other

---

[17] Deut. 6:4.
[18] Psalm 103:13–14.
[19] Jer. 31:3.
[20] Hos. 11:1; Luke 15.
[21] Jer. 3:19–20.
[22] Amos 3:2.
[23] Heb. 4:14–16.
[24] Isa. 53:1–12.

chapters of Isaiah as prophecies of Christ. Attention has been deliberately centered upon the Old Testament thus far in this discussion so the nurse may see how clearly it reveals God. The New Testament, however, presents what Christians believe is the final and complete manifestation of God in Jesus Christ.

For futher study: If a nurse would like to study the nature of God from the point of view of both the Old and the New Testaments, she will enjoy *The Christian's God* [25] by Stephen C. Neill.

For an over-all view of the Old Testament from a Protestant point of view, *Knowing the Old Testament* [26] by James P. Berkeley or *The Distinctive Ideas of the Old Testament* [27] by H. Norman Snaith is to be recommended.

The Gospel of Christ

As the Jews of the first century studied biblical and nonbiblical writings concerning the future,[28] they found in them promises of a golden age for Israel and a final supernatural judgment of the world. There was the prophecy of Amos that God would one day repair the damage suffered by Israel [29] and the word of the Lord to Jeremiah that he would "raise up for David a righteous Branch, and he shall reign as king and deal wisely, and shall execute justice and righteousness in the land." [30] The Jewish Targum looked upon portions of Isaiah as prophecies of a deliverer from God and translated Isaiah 42:1 as: "Behold my servant the Anointed (Messiah), I will draw him near . . ." [31] The book of Daniel and the apocryphal book of Enoch taught that a heavenly "Son of man" would descend to judge the nations.[32]

Jesus applied these terms to himself. When a Samaritan woman said that she knew the Messiah was coming, Jesus said: "I who

---

[25] New York: Association Press, 1955.

[26] Philadelphia: Judson Press, 1954.

[27] Philadelphia: Westminster Press, 1946.

[28] These are discussed by Stanley B. Frost in *Old Testament Apocalyptic* (London: Epworth Press, 1952).

[29] Amos 9:11–15.

[30] Jer. 23:5.

[31] George F. Moore, *Judaism in the First Centuries of the Christian Era* (Cambridge: Harvard University Press, 1946), II, 327.

[32] Dan. 7:13.

speak to you am he."[33] When Peter confessed that Jesus was the Christ, the Lord began to teach his disciples that as the Son of man he must suffer many things.[34] Thus he combined two Old Testament teachings: the suffering of God's servant, spoken of in Isaiah 40–66, and the coming of a triumphant "Son of man," recorded in Daniel.

This confident teaching of Jesus was a constant stumbling block to the Jews.[35] As Otto Borchert has said,[36] the Saviour was both too great and too lowly to suit the expectations of Israel. Some were offended because he forgave sins at the same time that he healed diseases. They believed that Jesus assumed a greatness beyond his person, and then they muttered, "Who can forgive sins but God alone."[37] But they also accused him of being too lowly when they said, "This man receives sinners and eats with them."[38]

Within a generation after Jesus' death the Christian leaders knew that many Jews would not accept their Lord as the Messiah.[39] However, both Jews and Christians have accepted the Old Testament as inspired literature. Many Jewish people are still looking for the fulfilment of its promises, while Christians look to it as the preparation of God for his full revelation in Jesus. Followers of Christ find the completion in the New Testament of essential ideas developed in the Old Testament.

God revealed himself through the personality of his prophets and finally in the personality of his Son. The covenant with Israel has become a new covenant in the Christian fellowship. The initiative of God's grace in coming to Moses is seen again in the loving gift of his Son. The prophecy of a suffering Servant is personalized in Christ's suffering on the cross. The hope of a saving remnant and a kingdom of God is fulfilled in Christ's coming to establish his kingdom among men and reaffirm his coming in "the last days." The saving faith of Abraham, Moses, and David in God is vindicated in Jesus, who required belief rather

[33] John 4:26. [34] Mark 8:29–33.
[35] 1 Cor. 1:23.
[36] *The Original Jesus* (London: Lutterworth Press, 1933).
[37] Mark 2:7. [38] Luke 15:2.
[39] Acts 13:44–48.

than works. Jesus required the kind of belief which was so social in its implications that it inevitably led to works of love.[40]

Although Christians and Jews can work together harmoniously in a hospital or a society, this does not mean that their essential beliefs are similar. The unity of the Christian's Bible is not found in a repetition of the Old Testament in the New Testament nor in the continuation of the mission of Israel by the Christian church. Even though the New Testament uses many foundational ideas from the Old Testament, the keystone is Jesus Christ, who was rejected by the rulers of Jews.[41]

The questions which nurses raise about the gospel, salvation, and the church will be discussed in the rest of this chapter from a distinctly Christian point of view. Many detailed questions, such as those about the life of Christ or Catholic-Protestant beliefs about Mary, should be discussed with a chaplain, priest, or pastor. Whenever possible, references will be made to books for further assistance.

(1) The dominant theme of the New Testament is the story of salvation. As ably presented by Archibald Hunter,[42] the story of salvation treats of a Saviour, a saved and saving people, and the means of salvation. The New Testament message has a basic unity. It is the unfolding of God's saving purpose for his people through the sending of his Messiah. The cornerstone of this divine activity is Christ: "In many and various ways God spoke of old to our fathers by the prophets; but in these last days he has spoken to us by a Son, whom he appointed the heir of all things, through whom also he created the world." [43] The message of salvation centers in a Saviour. For purposes of clarity the gospel—the message of salvation—will be considered first and then the Saviour himself.

Although there are many descriptions of salvation in the Bible, the earliest Christian formulations of the gospel are in the writings of Paul and in Acts. The chief passages in this relation

---

[40] Matt. 25. [41] 1 Peter 2:4–10.

[42] *The Message of the New Testament* (Philadelphia: Westminster Press, 1954).

[43] Heb. 1:1–2.

in Paul's epistles are Romans 1:2–5; Romans 10:8–9; and 1 Corinthians 15:3 ff. Like these are the early speeches in Acts 2:14–39, 3:12–26, 6:8–12, and 10:36–43.

The content of the message of salvation in these ancient Christian sermons had three elements. First, the speakers claimed that their message was the fulfilment of Old Testament prophecy: "This is what was spoken by the prophet . . ." (Acts 2:16).

Second, there was a historical exposition setting forth Jesus in his life, death, resurrection, and exaltation. Jesus, the promised Saviour, was born of David's line (Acts 2:30); he went about doing good by God's power (Acts 10:37); he was crucified (Acts 5:30), according to the Scriptures (Acts 3:18) and God's settled purpose (Acts 2:23); he has been raised by God's power from the dead (Acts 2:24; 1 Cor. 15:4); he is exalted to the right hand of God (Acts 2:33; Rom. 8:34); he will come again as judge and Saviour (Acts 3:20; 1 Thess. 1:10; Rom. 2:16).

Third, there was a summons to repent and accept the forgiveness of sins in Jesus.[44]

This account of the primitive form of the good news is given because the Gospels, as they are known today—Matthew, Mark, Luke, and John—are expanded forms of the essential message that was presented by the church during the time when many living people had known Christ. The elements mentioned above are found throughout the New Testament. They form the essential unity of the New Testament record.

But at the heart of the gospel lies the first and fundamental affirmation that Jesus is the Christ, the Messiah of God. The one common religious purpose of the New Testament writers was to declare that "Jesus is Lord."

Although there was no speculation about the divine versus the human elements in Jesus' person, the primitive church asserted that he was both Lord and Christ (Acts 2:36); in his divine name was the forgiveness of sins (Acts 2:38), yet he was also fully human, "a man attested to you by God" (Acts 2:22).

The writings of Paul give a more detailed and greatly enriched

---

[44] Acts 2:38.

account of the person of Christ. Paul spoke of Jesus as the Son, "the second Adam," "the cornerstone"; in him the whole fulness of deity dwells bodily (Col. 2:9). Paul assigned to Christ a place with God in the creation. This was especially helpful in combating the heresy in Colossae (Col. 1:15–20) which would have made Jesus a being created by God. The writer to the Hebrews set forth the significance of Jesus both in terms of his coming to fulfil the role of an ideal high priest of God and to be a sinless human being through whom men might receive strength in the time of trial (Heb. 4:18). Here was the one who would serve as the mediator between God and man (Heb. 9:15; 12:24).[45]

For the writers of the Gospels Jesus was both a man born of woman and yet the Son of God. When the miracle of God's sending his Son upon the earth, a basic truth of the New Testament, is admitted, then his virgin birth is seen as one part of his total personality. The important picture of Christ in the Gospels is of One who was fully human. He wept at the grave of Lazarus and was angry because of the hardness of the hearts of the Pharisees. He befriended children and the despised sinners of his day. Yet he was truly God, as seen in his words, his personality, his miracles, and greatest of all, in the resurrection.[46] To miss either of these emphases is to miss both the message and the Person revealed in the New Testament.

The doctrine of the incarnation, that is, the belief that God became a human being in order that men might become adopted children of God, has clinical significance. The nurse, the doctor, and the chaplain often personify God's interest in a person or remind the patient that Christ was a man and knows human troubles. One depressed patient kept telling his psychiatrist that no one understood him. The doctor had talked to the patient several times. Finally the man said, "Even *God* does not understand." The doctor replied, "Well, I believe that *I* understand something of what you say. And I know that Jesus who walked

---

[45] For a more complete discussion of the humanity and divinity of Jesus, read Stephen Neill, *Who Is Jesus Christ?* (New York: Association Press, 1957).

[46] The historical evidences of the resurrection are presented by James Martin, *Did Jesus Rise from the Dead?* (New York: Association Press, 1956).

the earth as a man has much more understanding than I have. So I believe God does understand."

For further reading: One of the chief questions submitted by student nurses concerned the life of Jesus. The imaginative and thoughtful *Life and Times of Jesus the Messiah*[47] by Alfred Edersheim is heavy but thorough. A simpler work is *The Life of Christ*[48] by Adam Fahling. *The Interpreter's Bible*,[49] volume I, contains articles on the life and ministry of Jesus. *The Original Jesus*[50] by Otto Borchert is a gripping portrayal of the mystery of Jesus' personality. In tracing the life of Jesus in Matthew, Mark, and Luke it is helpful to use the *Gospel Parallels*,[51] which prints similar passages under common headings. An accepted volume for Catholic nurses is Giuseppe Ricciotti's *Life of Christ*.[52]

(2) A Saviour and a message of salvation imply a saved people. In the Old Testament the people who worshiped God gathered into an "assembly" or "congregation." In the New Testament they were gathered by God's Spirit into a "congregation" or "church." The ancient Christians believed that they were the new Israel of God, the true heirs through Jesus Christ of the promises made to Abraham.[53] The nature of their relationship to Christ has been described in two books which will help nurses to emphasize the personal relationship of a patient to his church, rather than try to define the differences between denominations.[54]

The first religious responsibility of a nurse is to help a patient use the religion that he already has. She will soon discover that many people have never thought of ways in which their church can help them in a time of crisis and would like to know. Illness

---

[47] New York: Longmans, Green and Company, 1950.

[48] New York: Concordia, 1949.

[49] New York: Abingdon-Cokesbury Press, 1951.

[50] London: Lutterworth Press, 1933.

[51] New York: Thomas Nelson & Sons, 1949.

[52] Milwaukee: Bruce Publishing Company, 1947.

[53] 1 Peter 2:9–10.

[54] Paul Minear, *Jesus and His People* (New York: Association Press, 1956), and Robert Brown, *The Significance of the Church* (Philadelphia: Westminster, 1956).

often causes people to think seriously about spiritual welfare. Here is an example:

The premature baby of Mrs. B. died soon after birth. Mrs. B. was registered as "nonchurch member." A student nurse asked the hospital chaplain to visit Mrs. B.

When the chaplain arrived, Mrs. B. told him that she hated to lose her first child but felt that it might be God's way of telling her that parenthood was a bigger job than she had thought.

CHAPLAIN: You need to put some things in order first?

MRS. B.: I don't know where I am, religious-wise. I haven't been to church since I was married. (*Stares off into space.*)

CHAPLAIN: Uh-mm.

MRS. B.: Well, I was raised in a Catholic home, but I didn't want to insist that my husband change from his Lutheran church. We were married outside the church. Religion is just avoided.

CHAPLAIN: But the conflict is still there?

MRS. B.: Well (*pause*) it's strange to talk about the church after so long. . . . You know, I guess the church didn't mean to me what it could have. I never realized until this happened that we both have left something out.

CHAPLAIN: God?

MRS. B. (*smiling*): I'm glad you said it. What do you think I should do?

CHAPLAIN: Have you been thinking of ways to make amends?

MRS. B.: Yes, about going to church again.

CHAPLAIN: Is that all?

MRS. B.: No . . . I must talk to my husband! It would be such a relief to discuss it openly. (*pause*) I thought at first that you would preach me a sermon about not worrying about my child . . .

A month later Mrs. B. was readmitted for vaginal bleeding. The chaplain picked her name out of the daily admission cards and paid her a visit.

MRS. B.: Hello! I have wanted to see you. I have news. You remember I was going to talk with my husband? Guess what?

CHAPLAIN: I know it will be interesting.

MRS. B.: We're both attending the little Lutheran church out on State Street. I've had the time of my life. I'm studying their doctrine now but haven't been confirmed yet.

In a personal crisis the church came to have a new meaning for both this woman and her husband.

This was the way in which the first Christians thought of their church. It was a community in which God reigned over the disputes of men (Matt. 18:15–20). It was a school for Christian living. Within it were people of diverse opinions and talents, but they possessed a spiritual unity in their devotion to the Lord Jesus (1 Cor. 12:12–26). Those who were "in Christ" distinguished themselves by their patience, lowliness, and meekness (Eph. 4:1–16). Within this fellowship there was understanding forgiveness (Gal. 5:25 to 6:5) and a common sharing of suffering (1 Peter 5:9; James 5:13–18). These are the sources of spiritual power which a church can bring to the sick today.

But some people have found the Christian fellowship to be marred by murmuring (Acts 6:1–6), hypocrisy (Acts 5:1–11), the power of money (Acts 8:14–25), and contention or party spirit (Acts 15). The nurse may find herself precipitated into an unresolved church conflict like the following:

STUDENT NURSE: Mr. E., would you like for us to turn on your pillow speaker so that you can hear the morning devotional?

MR. E's SISTER: Yes, it'd do him good!

MR. E.: Guess it wouldn't do any harm.

SISTER (*to nurse*): He used to be a real Methodist. Did lots of things in the church. Now he's a backslider.

MR. E. (*looking nurse in the eye*): You want to know why I quit the Methodist church?

NURSE: Ah . . . well . . .

MR. E.: I quit because they substituted the Ku Klux Klan for Jesus Christ.

NURSE'S THOUGHT: At this point the sister squeezed my arm—apparently she had opened Pandora's box. I tried to ease away.

MR. E.: Yes, sir, I told the preacher just how I felt, but he did nothing. I don't think it ought to be promoted in the church.

SISTER: It's all over. You shouldn't hold it against the church for thirty years.

MR. E.: That's not the way to do things in church. I knew I wasn't welcome there. They didn't ask my advice any more. They—

NURSE'S THOUGHT: Mr. E. was talking at a fast rate. I didn't know whether to slip out the door or go over and try to quiet him down.

SISTER: That's your idea of it. But you need to go to church and read the Bible now.

MR. E.: Yes, yes. But they had no business substituting the Klan for the Spirit of Christ. Isn't that right? (*He skewered me with a glance.*)

NURSE: Sir, I have to ask the other patients if they want to hear the religious broadcast.

SISTER (*releasing the student's arm*): Oh, yes. I didn't intend to start this. Thank you very much, dear.

NURSE'S THOUGHT: It all took about a minute, but it seemed like an hour.

We do not know whether the church or this man was the main source of difficulty. But it is evident that religion was being used to beat the patient rather than to bind up his wounds.

On occasion, nurses are asked about different denominations by patients. In addition, nurses themselves often wonder about other religious groups. Patients, other nurses, or boy friends may be of another faith.

It is best for a chaplain or a minister to answer the specific questions of patients about different denominations. A nurse may say: "I'm glad to know of your interest in religion. Our chaplain will be here this morning. Would you like to continue this discussion with him?" or, "Well, I can't answer that question with authority."

Many nurses sent in questions about differences between Catholics and Protestants. A popular question-and-answer booklet written by a Protestant is *What's the Difference?*[55] by Arthur G. Reynolds. A Catholic booklet is *Finding Christ's Church*[56] by John A. O'Brien. A Protestant, S. I. Steuber, has written a *Primer on Roman Catholicism for Protestants.*[57]

Since some Protestants become Catholics and some Catholics become Protestants, John W. Brush has written a pamphlet, *When You Come Over*[58] for Catholics who have become Protestants. Hilaire Belloc and others have written *Why I Am a Catholic*[59] for the average reader. *A Primer for Protestants*[60] by

[55] Toronto: United Church of Canada, 1954.
[56] Notre Dame, Indiana: Ave Maria Press, 1950.
[57] New York: Association Press, 1953.
[58] New York: National Council of Churches, 1951.
[59] New York: The Macmillan Company, 1932.
[60] New York: Association Press, 1953.

James Nichols will familiarize the average Protestant with basic tenets of his faith. The principle of voluntary, nonstate-supported churches is well described by Winthrop Hudson in *The Great Tradition of the American Churches.*[61] The beautifully illustrated *Religions of Mankind*, published by Life magazine, has a two-page chart of the major Christian groups and their major beliefs. Information about other denominations would probably be in *The Small Sects in America* [62] by E. T. Clark.

If a nurse wanted to trace the history of churches, she might like to start with Roland Bainton's *The Church of Our Fathers,*[63] which is a simple description of the general development of Christianity. An authoritative, one-volume reference work is *A History of Christianity* [64] by Kenneth Scott Latourette.

The major Protestant denominations are described by Virgilius Ferm in *The American Church of the Protestant Heritage* [65] and by Frank Mead in *Handbook of Denominations in the United States.*[66]

It is a mistake to identify a person's theology by his denomination alone. Protestants tend to define themselves by schools of thought, such as conservative, orthodox, liberal, or fundamental, as well as by denominations. These terms are described in nontechnical language by William Hordern in *A Layman's Guide to Protestant Theology.*[67]

There are a number of books which describe one denomination, such as the series published by Thomas Nelson: Victor Beck, *Why I Am a Lutheran;* Park Hays Miller, *Why I Am a Presbyterian;* Louie D. Newton, *Why I Am a Baptist;* Roy L. Smith, *Why I Am a Methodist.*[68]

If a nurse has an interest in the study of all religions, I would recommend John B. Noss' *Man's Religions.*[69]

---

[61] New York: Harper & Brothers, 1953.
[62] New York: Abingdon Press, 1949.
[63] New York: Charles Scribner's Sons, 1944.
[64] New York: Harper & Brothers, 1953.
[65] New York: Philosophical Library, 1953.
[66] New York: Abingdon Press, 1956.
[67] New York: The Macmillan Company, 1956.
[68] New York: Thomas Nelson & Sons, 1957.
[69] New York: The Macmillan Company, 1949.

People get along better when they respect the sincerity of another's religion and are sensitive to differences in theological beliefs and practices. In American hospitals these differences are usually respected, but a recognition of different points of view should not lead to special privilege for one group. For example, one nurse asked: "Why is it that the Catholic students can go to Mass on Sunday mornings and the Protestant students, who are supposed to be allowed to go to the Protestant services, are usually never allowed off the floors? It is just as busy early in the morning as it is at ten A.M." So far as hospital practices are concerned, both groups should share equally the privilege of church attendance while on duty.

(3) Nearly a third of the New Testament references to salvation refer to deliverance from specific ills, such as disease, captivity, or death.[70] Nurses have many opportunities to work with patients who need this kind of salvation. One student nurse gave this example:

A doctor came down the hall and asked if someone would go to this lady's room and talk with her, as she was very depressed. I went to her room and just chatted with her for a while. A young woman, she told me her husband had shot himself (in a hunting accident), her brother had recently died an alcoholic, and she was left to run two businesses. She was exhausted physically, mentally, and spiritually. I talked with her then for a while, sharing with her a bit of what the Lord has done for me and other examples of the love of God meeting the need in the lives of others. She told me that she knew Christ as her Saviour but that she was confused. I gave her a good tract that I had and suggested that she read it in her leisure. She eagerly accepted it and said she would read it.

She was so pleased that someone had come and talked with her for a very few minutes; just the fact that the purpose was to see and talk with her and not to take temperature, give medicines, or treatments seemed to mean so much to her. She thanked me for coming and for the tract and asked me to come back and see her again. I told her that I would, but the next time I was back I found that she had been dismissed and had left the hospital so there was no further opportunity to talk with her.

---

[70] Matt. 9:21; Luke 8:36; Acts 27:20.

Here was a woman who needed very specific salvation from the pressure of business, personal loneliness, and sorrow. The nurse's opportunity was to show how these problems can be met through God's grace. Her personal concern for the woman was effective spiritual medicine for loneliness and depression.

Salvation may also be spoken of in more general terms. Salvation is from sin (Matt. 1:21), from darkness to light (1 Peter 2:9), from guilt to pardon (Eph. 1:7), from slavery to freedom (Gal. 5:1), and from alienation to a share in divine citizenship (1 Peter 2:10; Eph. 2:12–13).

The relation of salvation to life may be seen in the mind of this patient:

NURSE: Good morning, Mr. R. How are you this morning?

MR. R.: Fine, I guess.

NURSE: Why, Mr. R., what's wrong? Are you worrried about your surgery?

MR. R.: Yes, I'm afraid they will find cancer. I don't know what my wife and two girls will do if I die. Why did God do this to me?

NURSE: There are many people who have cancer and have lived many years after their surgery. As for why God "did this to you," we never know why he does what he does.

MR. R.: I know that only about 1 per cent of people with cancer die, but who knows that I won't be that 1 per cent? I haven't done everything that I should have, especially for my wife. I have always drunk a lot, and my wife has suffered for it. Do you think I have a chance to go to heaven?

NURSE: I think you have as good a chance as myself or anyone else has, and I'm sure your wife understands. Are you afraid of death, Mr. R.?

MR. R.: No, I guess I'm not really afraid, only for my wife and children.

NURSE: You have two of the best doctors, and through them I feel God will do all he can to help you go home to your wife and children.

MR. R.: My doctors might not be able to do anything for me.

NURSE: Have you talked to your doctors about the way you feel? I know they can explain your surgery to you better than I can.

MR. R.: I'm afraid they'll think I'm crazy.

That afternoon the student saw Mr. R. again.

MR. R.: I feel better now that I've talked to you and my doctors.

Mr. R. needs salvation from guilt to pardon; he is so guilty that he thinks that God may kill him. He also feels alienated from his wife because of his sinful actions. If Mr. R. can see that he has caused God to suffer even more than his wife has suffered, he will know something of what the atonement means. Atonement is a theological term for the suffering of Christ on behalf of sinful men whom he loves.[71]

The idea of the suffering of God distinguishes the Christian view from worldly views of salvation. Some people would like for God to be a good-humored, indulgent father. The Christian's God is righteous as well as long-suffering. He does not pass lightly over sin because he has created man in his image, and faithlessness wounds him. It costs the person who is hurt more to forgive than it does the one who inflicts the wound. God alone can afford complete forgiveness. He has given his Son for man's salvation. Those who believe this testimony of God's love shall have eternal life.[72]

God loves mankind. He deals with men personally, as a Father with his children. Because of this he destined, in love, men to be his children through Jesus Christ, whom he sent into the world for their redemption.[73] Just as Mr. R. brought suffering upon his wife, so the rebellion of men brings suffering to God.

When we know that we have outraged God's love, when we realize that forgiveness must come from him, when we accept the forgiveness that he has already prepared through his Son, Jesus Christ, then we are saved.[74]

Christians believe that there is no salvation apart from Jesus Christ.[75] Without him there is neither power over sin in this world nor fellowship with God in the next. Those who have never heard the gospel have no light but the feeble and often perverted leading of their own consciences. By their works they will be judged of God.[76] Those who worship anything less than God are subject to his wrath.[77] God is not an idle spectator of

---

[71] Rom. 5:6–11; John 3:16–17.
[72] John 6:50–60.
[73] Eph. 1:3–10.
[74] Eph. 2:5–9.
[75] John 3:18; 10:7–18; Acts 4:12.
[76] Rom. 2:13–16; cf. Matt. 25:31–46.
[77] Rom. 1:18–32.

the human drama. He is not like the parent who deplores the sins of his children but does not wish to interfere with their "self-expression." He is not a passive person who cannot bring himself to take stern measures because people violate the rights of other persons whom he has created. A part of God's concern for men is expressed in such biblical words as *punish*, *chastise*, *wrath*, *anger*, and *indignation*. All this comes because God loves men enough to commit himself to participate in their struggles.

Final judgment is in God's hands. Self-righteous individuals have sometimes equated God's wrath with their own—like the husband who asked a nurse if God would not cause his wife to suffer a long time in the hospital because she had not obeyed his whims. People usually reject those who tell them how God is going to condemn them, but they listen with interest to those who testify how God has lifted them from condemnation to newness of life.

Although there are many aspects of salvation, there is one more which deserves special mention. This is the difference between Roman Catholic and Protestant teachings about the means of salvation.

Roman Catholics and Protestants are agreed that salvation comes from God through Jesus Christ. But they differ on the role of the church in this process. The strict Catholic teaching is that "no one can be saved without sanctifying grace, and the Catholic Church alone is the divinely established means by which grace is brought to the world and the full fruits of Our Lord's Redemption are applied to men." [78]

Protestants believe in a direct, intimate relationship between the believer and Christ. They believe that Jesus alone is the mediator between God and man.[79] Therefore, Protestants reject the veneration of Mary and the role of priests as direct authorities of Christ. Although both Roman Catholics and Protestants state that salvation is by grace rather than by man's efforts, Protestants object to the Roman Catholic emphasis upon good works, in-

---

[78] Quoted by Stanley I. Stuber in *Primer on Roman Catholicism for Protestants* (New York: Association Press, 1953), p. 7.

[79] 1 Tim. 2:5; Eph. 2:18; 1 John 2:1; Heb. 4:14–16.

dulgences, and the treasury of merit. Here again the means of salvation varies although both groups pray for the church to be free from sin and agree that there is human error in the church and its ministers. The Roman Catholic believes that his church and the Pope are able to obtain essential perfection in matters of faith and morals. Complete obedience to a perfect church through prayer, attendance at mass, and partaking of the sacraments are his means of attaining grace.

Protestants are never this sure about their church or their ministers. God's grace is a gift which never guarantees immunity against further sin. Neither in faith nor in morals can man ever be assured of perfection. The pride of a bishop, the pretensions of a theologian, and the will-to-power of a "main street" preacher are the corrupting evidences of a basic self-love which is never completely eradicated from man. Although salvation brings freedom from the condemnation of God, self-love is mixed with the new power of the love of God which enters the believer's heart. Neither man nor his church can stand apart from the judgment of God *in any respect.*[80]

From this short discussion of a very long debate in history, nurses can see that all Christians agree that salvation comes from God but disagree whether men should be mediators (Catholic) or ministers (Protestant) of his grace.

For further reading: Two general works on the books of the New Testament are *The Literature of the New Testament*[81] by Ernest F. Scott and *Understanding the Books of the New Testament*[82] by Patrick H. Carmichael and others. *The Theology of the New Testament*[83] by G. B. Stevens presents the central ideas of each New Testament writer.

So far this discussion has been organized about great biblical doctrines—the nature of God, of Christ, and of the church. We

---

[80] See "Wisdom, Grace and Power" in Reinhold Niebuhr, *The Nature and Destiny of Man* (New York: Charles Scribner's Sons, 1953) II, 99–156; and Rom. 6:8; 8:6; Eph. 4:24; Rom. 6:11–12; Gal. 5:24–26; 1 John 1:8; Phil. 3:12; 2:12–13; 1 Pet. 2:10; 1 Thess. 5:23.

[81] New York: Columbia University, 1936.

[82] Richmond: John Knox Press, 1952.

[83] New York: Charles Scribner's Sons, 1927.

have observed the way in which these truths are related to nursing practice and daily living. The next group of chapters will organize the material about great problems in religion and nursing, such as pain and suffering, guilt, depression, death, and the influence of mind on body.

3. The Spiritual Significance of Illness

ILLNESS MAY PRECIPITATE a spiritual crisis. Since illness is man's reaction to disease, it is a time when men are brought face to face with the ultimate concerns of life. Inescapable issues rise up before them, such as the anxiety of death, the despair of loneliness, the threat that there will be no meaning to life unless they can keep up the same business pace, as well as the uncertainty as to whether or not a marriage will hold together.

This emphasis upon the religious dimensions of illness is based upon both medicine and theology. Psychosomatic medicine has studied the close connection between the way a person feels and the way the body reacts to the emotions. Biblical scholars have shown a renewed interest in the Scriptures which assume that man is a total being who cannot be divided into "body" and "soul."

In this chapter some of the biblical passages which teach the unity of personality will be studied. In addition, the statements of doctors concerning the spiritual significance of illness will be considered. Examples will be given from which a nurse can learn to identify spiritual concerns. Finally there will be a brief discussion of faith healing.

Body and Soul

There is some disapproval of the emphasis upon illness as a spiritual crisis. Objections come from two sources. On the one hand, some people have developed a philosophical system which may be called "scientism." They will object that a religious dimension of personality is "unscientific." On the other hand, there are those who identify religion with the philosophy of Greek dualism. They believe that there is a rigid distinction between the body and the soul. They object to a close identification of the "lower" passions of the body with the "higher" thinking of the detachable soul.

The first problem of a scientific philosophy is related to biological and physiological knowledge about man. Those who believe in this philosophy are unwilling to accept any evidence about man that cannot be "scientifically" demonstrated through the methods of physiological research or chemical analysis. Since the soul cannot be demonstrated in a test tube, it is assumed that man is nothing but an animal who has developed some abilities more fully than other animals.

The chief weakness in this type of thinking is its failure to recognize that physiological evidence is not the only available data on the nature of man. A nurse can be grateful for the tremendous knowledge which she has received from the physical sciences without accepting a philosophy of life which reduces man to nothing but his physical components. The Bible contains the Genesis account that man was made of "the dust of the earth." His close connection to other animals and all of nature is not disputed by modern theologians. But the Christian also remembers that man is made in the image of God and receives his life by "the breath of God."

Another objection of scientism arises from the philosophical conclusions of some sociologists and psychologists. The studies of Freud and his associates have demonstrated the important influence of a person's early years in shaping and developing personality. But this clinical conclusion has led some persons to the philosophical assumption that a man's character is absolutely determined by the influences of his first three years of life. Sigmund Freud was devoted to what is called "biological determinism." He believed that a man is basically moved by biological instincts, of which the sexual urge is the most important.

It is important for the nurse to consider the depth of psychological and medical understanding of personality which has emerged from the work of Freud and his followers. But an acceptance of the scientific discoveries and therapeutic methods of depth psychotherapy does not mean that its philosophical assumptions must also be accepted.

The error in determinism is the belief that people can do nothing but follow the forces that shape their personalities in the first three years of life. This absolute view is contradicted by other psychologists, such as Gardner Murphy and Gordon Allport. These men assert that life is *conditioned* by early influences but that heredity and early training do not *determine* all that develops later. This is compatible with Christian doctrine. The Old Testament stories of the patriarchs are eloquent testimony that sons may fall into the same sins as their fathers. Isaac lied about his wife just as his father Abraham had done. Isaac was continually avoiding a fight with the Philistines. His son Jacob followed the same pattern by tricking Esau and then fleeing to another land. Not until late maturity did he gain the courage to come back to Palestine and face his brother. His change in attitude can be attributed to the experience he had when he wrestled with the angel at the river Jabbok. It was the first time that he stood up to a decision with manly courage. He broke the passive pattern which his father had set for him.

The third philosophical problem with scientism concerns the ethics of relativism in morality. The pioneer sociologist, William Graham Sumner, demonstrated that various social groups in America have different standards of right and wrong. Anthropological studies of cultures other than our own, such as those of South Sea Islanders, have led many people to assume that all morality is relative. The king in *Anna and the King of Siam* complained that when he was a boy "what was not was not," but in his later years he found that "what was not is *probably* not."

Instead of demonstrating that all morality is relative, the anthropologist and the sociologist help us understand Jesus' teaching to the effect that it is hazardous to base morality upon the customs of one group or nation. Jesus criticized the Pharisees for their slavish conformity to certain customs of their day. In the same way, modern sociologists have pointed out that "religious" sanctions of certain modes of dress or of conduct were actually the product of a particular age in history. This is a problem also of institutions other than the church. In the 1890's some nursing schools forbade student nurses to date medical students. Even the most obedient and devout nursing student might have difficulty in accepting such a rule today!

The other school of thought which might be offended by the intimate connection of spirit and matter can be labeled "religious." It is quite possible for a person to be "religious" without accepting Christ or the Christian view of life. Actually, the "religious" point of view is more nearly identified with the dualism of Greek philosophy, but it has become synonymous with religion in the minds of many people. The person who accepts this division of body and soul will often seek to ignore physical or emotional distress and exalt his "spiritual" strength. Nurses can often detect this thinking in patients who say, "There's nothing really wrong with me. It's only a spiritual problem. The doctor keeps telling me that I can't keep my house perfectly in order with three young children. But if I would just have a quiet time to pray each day, I would be all right." The patient is denying her actual problems and is seeking to "spiritualize" them.

Nurses will see one form of this philosophy among the believers in faith healing who reject medical aid. Such persons believe that the mind and body are separate and that the mind can control the body completely. This will be considered in more detail in a later section of this chapter.

The Biblical Concept of Personality

In contradistinction to "religious" dualism, Hebrew-Christian thought emphasizes the unity of personality. Man is made of both the dust of the earth and the breath of God. He is a living, inseparable being.

In ancient Hebrew thought there was no separation between body and soul. The writer of the thirty-fifth Psalm wrote: "All my bones shall say, 'O Lord, who is like thee, thou who deliverest the weak from him who is too strong for him, the weak and needy from him who despoils him?"[1] Today we do not think of bones when we think of praising God, but the Hebrews did. Heart, breath, soul, and spirit were considered parts of personality and were fitting instruments of God's praise. Bowels, liver, belly, and kidneys provided somatic expressions of personal emotions. The Hebrew did not deny the role of physiological or biological drives in his religious life. He loved God with all of himself.[2]

The Bible also assumes an intimate connection between the conscious and unconscious portions of the personality. The unconscious, the depths of the soul, was alive with understanding of events that troubled the conscious soul. The unconscious often made itself known through dreams. The Hebrew believed that those who dreamed thoughts or actions that were later demonstrated in reality had strong souls. The health of the soul would determine the reality of the dream.[3] God spoke to Solomon through a dream, and the next day the king incorporated the philosophy of the dream into his inaugural address.[4]

The New Testament continued the Old Testament thought of man as a total being. Jesus healed the whole man. He infuriated scribes by saying to a paralytic, "My son, your sins are forgiven."[5] He told the Pharisees that he could heal a man by either forgiving his sins or commanding his body to be healed.[6]

The apostle Paul often used a word to designate personality that is translated as "body" in English. For example, he commanded husbands to love their wives as they loved their own bodies. The word that he used for body can be better translated as "personality."

Sometimes Paul has been quoted in support of "religious" dualism because he wrote about the warfare between the flesh and the spirit.[7] But he did not mean to equate the flesh with

---

[1] Psalm 35:10.
[2] Deut. 6:4.
[3] Jer. 23:32.
[4] 1 Kings 3.
[5] Mark 2:5.
[6] Total healing does not always take place. A man may be forgiven for his sins without being able to walk, or vice versa.
[7] Rom. 8:1–17.

biological drives and the spirit with a disembodied soul. Paul was not talking about a conflict between asceticism and physical sensuality. When he contrasted the works of the spirit against the works of the flesh in the fifth chapter of Galatians, he directly related to some physical activity only five of the ten sins "of the flesh." The "mind of the flesh" was the way he designated a denial of man's dependence on God. The carnally-minded man was one who trusted in that which was of human effort or origin. Further, in Philippians 1:19–25 and Galatians 2:20 Paul stressed the glorification of the "flesh" through surrender by faith in Christ.

The Spiritual Significance of Illness

Since the Hebrews believed in the unity of personality, they also believed that spiritual problems affected physical health. Physical illness was looked upon as a sign of spiritual disease. Therefore, after speaking of his emotional distress, the psalmist related his physical deprivation: "I can count all my bones." [8] Again, when the writer was physically ill, he pleaded that the Lord would not rebuke him in anger or forsake him in wrath.[9]

In Jesus' day this connection between the physical and the spiritual phases of man's being was carried to the extreme. The disciples wondered whether a blind man or his parents had sinned, since the Jews of that day assumed that one or the other must have committed sin that caused the physical malady. Jesus answered: "It was not that this man sinned, or his parents, but that the works of God might be made manifest in him." [10]

The ancient church believed that there was such a close connection between personal relationships and physical disease that they commanded the elders of the church to be called when a man was sick. The elders both applied the medicine of that day, oil, and prayed that the sins of the man might be forgiven.[11] Prayer and medicine went together.

The spiritual significance of illness may also be illustrated from the works of doctors. Dr. Gotthard Booth has written that man stays objectively healthy as long as he believes himself capable of

---

[8] Psalm 22:17.
[9] Psalm 38.
[10] John 9:3.
[11] James 5:13–18.

pursuing those purposes which are vital to him.[12] His state of health may be continued even in the presence of organic disturbances which might handicap a different personality. By contrast, another person who cannot normally adjust to the present and anticipated demands of his world will react to his situation with illness. He becomes preoccupied with himself.

The Christian emphasis upon purposeful living is such a strong motivating force in life that many believe that it does help in combatting disease. It should be noted, however, that health in itself is not the sole objective of Christianity. Jesus spoke of man's concern for food, health, clothing, and the length of life in the Sermon on the Mount. But he concluded: "Seek first his kingdom and his righteousness, and all these things shall be yours as well." [13]

Another contribution to our understanding of religion and illness has been made by Dr. Viktor Frankl. To Dr. Frankl, health includes not only what man wants from the world but also what the world demands from man. He is concerned with the "will to meaning." In *The Doctor and the Soul* [14] Dr. Frankl has stressed education toward responsibility, which he calls "logotherapy." The biblical question, "What does the Lord require of you?" is of great therapeutic significance. Dr. Frankl reminds his fellow physicians that they may disregard this emphasis upon responsibility and the spiritual meaning of life, but they should remember in doing so that the only thing which would then differentiate them from a veterinarian would be their clientele.

In the writings of many physicians, as in the Bible, there is a concern about a patient's thoughts and feelings during illness. It is no longer good form to speak of "hepatitis case in bed two." It is important to think of the man in bed number two as a father who is concerned about his job and his children and as a husband who worries about his wife because she is taking in washing to meet expenses. All of these concerns influence his recovery.

---

[12] *The Church and Mental Health* (New York: Charles Scribner's Sons, 1953).

[13] Matt. 6:33.

[14] New York: Alfred Knopf, 1955.

The Identification of Spiritual Concerns

Spiritual dimensions of illness are often recognized by the nurse. In order that she may have trained ears to hear the patient when he talks about his spiritual stresses, some examples may be helpful.

One student nurse wrote of an aggressive, abrupt woman in her fifties who faced the amputation of one of her legs. Her husband had died a year previously. Her two daughters lived in a distant city. The day before her operation she said to her nurse: "I don't care what the doctors say. I know that I will be a complete invalid. I will be a terrible burden to my daughters. They want me to come to Chicago and live with them. But I have spent all my life here. Can you imagine an invalid woman in a strange city? I wish God would let me die on the operating table." This woman was concerned about more than losing a leg. She did not want to be dependent upon her children the rest of her life. This stress, this fear of the future, disturbed her more than the operation.

In another instance a nurse became well acquainted with a forty-year-old woman who was admitted to the hospital for a diagnostic examination. The nurse observed that each day the patient became physically and mentally worse. At first the woman expressed the hope that her stay in the hospital would cause her estranged husband to take new interest in her. But after she had telephoned him each day, she would go back to her room more depressed. He never came to visit her. The diagnostic tests were not painful, but she seemed to be physically wasting away. When she received the news that she had an incurable disease, she said, "What have I done to deserve all this suffering and heartbreak? Why do I have to suffer this all alone?" She was a woman who had to face sickness and death without her husband. Since she had no other relatives, with the exception of a few friends she had no one to share her burden with her.

When a student nurse said good morning to a young woman who had been in the hospital for several days, the patient replied, "I am glad you came by because time seems to drag so much."

NURSE: Well, we will have to see what we can find to keep you occupied.

PATIENT: It seems there is trouble arising for me with my home and my family.

NURSE: Is there something I can do to help?

PATIENT: My husband seems to be getting tired of my being sick and in the hospital. When he comes to visit me, he gets irritated and walks out of the room several times during his visit. He has never been like that before. It worries me.

Both the husband and the wife were tense because of this illness, but instead of sharing their concerns with each other, the husband walked in and out of the room while his wife worried in silence. Her illness revealed their inability to handle a crisis together.

A student nurse wondered how she would approach a middle-aged unmarried schoolteacher who had been told by her doctor on the previous evening that she had a fast-growing and inoperable cancer. After the nurse had been in the room for a few minutes, the patient said, "Well, my doctor came by to see me last night."

NURSE: Is that so?

PATIENT: Yes, he told me the news. (*pause*) I guess that we all have to die sometime.

NURSE: Yes, Miss R.

PATIENT: I will need to tell my sister this when she visits me today.

NURSE: Is there anything that I can do, Miss R.?

PATIENT: Yes, I would like for you to call Pastor L. He has always been close to both of us. I want to take communion. I need that spiritual strength.

This patient could look death in the face and find real strength in her religion. It is especially significant that in this spiritual crisis she called for communion. To many patients communion implies something negative—a last rite before death. To this woman communion was a source of spiritual strength which she could call upon and use while she was still in full control of her faculties.

Faith Healing

This discussion leads naturally to the question of the relationship between faith and healing. Many nurses have asked questions about what is commonly called "divine healing." It is also a popular subject of discussion among doctors and pastors. But there have been very few clinical studies of faith healing which would command the attention of medically trained persons.

One of these was a memorandum submitted by a special committee of the Council of the British Medical Association to the Archbishop's Commission on Divine Healing.[15] The committee sent out questionnaires to British physicians and held conferences on the subject of divine healing. Seventy questionnaires were returned from physicians. Many of these gave examples of divine healing which had been seen in the work of missionary doctors in other countries. Although no attempt was made to define "divine healing," the committee attempted to explain it as cures by nonmedical methods of treatment in which there were some references to religion.

The committee then examined these nonmedical cures under the following categories: (1) mistaken diagnosis, (2) mistaken prognosis, (3) alleviation, (4) remission, (5) spontaneous cures, (6) combined treatment. The commission concluded, "We have seen no evidence that there is any special type of illness cured solely by spiritual healing which cannot be cured by medical methods which do not involve such claims." [16] The committee did not rule out the considerable evidence that religion was valuable in the treatment of various disorders. But since they had confined "divine healing" to alleged cures in which there was no medical intervention, their conclusion was inevitable.

In the United States, on the other hand, most clergymen think of divine healing as a combined activity of medicine and religion. Assuming this, there are more "faith healings" here than in England. Dr. Paul Johnson of Boston University reported the research of Professor Charles Braden of Northwestern University

---

[15] London: British Medical Association, 1956.
[16] *Ibid.*, p. 13.

in the Spring, 1956, issue of *Religion in Life*. Professor Braden found that out of 467 pastors who were questioned about spiritual healing, 34 per cent said that they had attempted to perform some type of healing. Mental illnesses comprised the largest number of cases of healing reported. Most of these had been medically diagnosed and treated. About half had been pronounced hopeless. In all but three cases the "spiritual" cure was recorded as permanent. The second largest category of diseases was organic, with cancer leading the list. In almost every case a diagnosis had been made by a competent physician, according to the pastors' reports.

In contrast with the assumptions of the British Medical Association, American pastors considered medical and theological treatment as necessary components of spiritual healing. Almost all of the pastors' cases had been medically diagnosed, and only a fraction of them had failed to receive some medical treatment.

When people are aware of the biblical and medical emphasis upon the interrelationship of the emotional, spiritual, and physical dimensions of personality, "divine" or "faith" healing may be regarded as one part of the hospital's total ministry to the patient. Most of the present difficulty has arisen from the philosophical assumption that the mind and body are separate. Faith is then excluded from medical science. In 1956 faith healer Jack Coe of Texas contracted bulbar polio and prayed for three weeks that a miracle would heal him. He was rushed to a hospital too late for the medical science which he had despised to have a chance to heal him.

In addition to the radical healing groups which conduct sensational tent meetings, there are more staid religious bodies who believe in the power of the detachable mind over the body. The most well known of these is Christian Science, which has a great appeal through its teaching that God has meaning for the whole of life. Christian Science solves the problem of suffering and evil by denying the essential reality of all pain and disease. Another dualistic group is the Unity School of Christianity. This group teaches that a spiritual body will replace the physical body if a person has a firm-enough belief. With such a sure faith, he need not die. Sickness is attacked through thought processes that produce living organisms which will kill disease-producing organisms. Theosophy, which offers self-redemption through mystical disciplines, is a kindred movement. Pain, sorrow, and all unhappy forces are accepted and explained as the inevitable result of wrong action either in this or in a previous existence. Both Unity and Theosophy believe in the reincarnation of men after death.

Some Catholics and Protestants are also active in healing today. The most celebrated Catholic center is Lourdes, France. Since 1882 a medical committee has examined all claims of spiritual cures at this center.[17] In America the most celebrated Catholic center is at Ste. Anne de Beaupre, Montmorance County, Quebec. Many visit these shrines, not in search of a physical cure, but of spiritual benefit.

Protestant healing groups may be found within one denomination, such as the fellowship of St. Luke in the Episcopal Church, or in interdenominational movements such as The Camps Farthest Out led by the late Glenn Clark. A discussion of all these healing groups may be found in *The Healing Power of Faith* by Will Oursler,[18] *Modern Religious Cults and Movements* by G. G. Atkins,[19] *The Church and Healing* by C. J. Scherzer,[20] and *Faith Healing and the Christian Faith*[21] by Wade Boggs.

Various methods of healing are recognized by evangelical groups such as the Church of God and the Assembly of God. Their leaders do not favor commercialized, highly-advertised healing campaigns. Instead, ministers and laymen look upon faith healing as one part of the total ministry of the church. An Assembly of God pastor described his belief in these words:

God has three methods of healing. When he created the human body, he placed in the blood stream power to fight against disease and power to heal after the disease's cause has been removed. That we would call "nature healing," and yet it is divine healing because it is

[17] The story of this shrine has been told by Ruth Cranston in *The Miracle of Lourdes* (New York: Popular Library, 1957).
[18] New York: Hawthorne Books, 1957.
[19] New York: Fleming H. Revell Co., 1923.
[20] Philadelphia: Westminster Press, 1950.
[21] Richmond: John Knox Press, 1957.

of a God-given origin. The cause of sickness may be from injury or from a disease, and the cause may be removed by nature or medical application, or even surgery, but nature's power must do the healing. But it is also God's healing, or divine healing. Second, the power of God in answer to the prayer of faith. Then, third, in answer to the prayer of faith the mighty power of God destroys the disease or affliction and heals the broken bone or cut—the blind eyes made to see, the deaf-mute made to hear and talk, the sick made well in an instant. Like the man at the beautiful gate when Peter said, "Silver and gold have I none; but such as I have give I thee: In the name of Jesus Christ of Nazareth rise up and walk. And he took him by the right hand, and lifted him up: and immediately his feet and ancle bones received strength. And he leaping up stood, and walked, and entered with them into the temple, walking, and leaping, and praising God" (Acts 3:6–8, AV). Such healings would be called a miracle. But few have such great faith.

Prayer, anointing with oil, and the laying of the pastor's hands on the patient's head are acceptable methods of healing in these groups.

As the nurse looks at faith healing, she may ask: "Is it not possible for God to still heal today?" Since God continues to work in his universe, he must be actively engaged in the healing processes. The problem is to distinguish between that which is a genuine spiritual healing and what is magical.

In trying to make this distinction, a nurse should first learn that there is a difference between magic and religion. In *Healing: Human and Divine* [22] Paul Tillich describes magic as a belief that all parts of the universe are sympathetic with each other and dependent upon each other. All the powers in the world are finite. With the right incantation or name, a magician professes to obtain whatever he wishes from the gods or other forces in nature. Magic is not religion. Religion is the relation to something that is ultimate, unconditioned, and transcendent. It is the relationship of human beings to a power that is infinite, eternal, and absolute. In the Hebrew-Christian tradition, God is always transcendent, though he comes to mankind in love: "For my thoughts are not your thoughts, neither are your ways my ways, says the Lord.

[22] Simon Doniger, ed. (New York: Association Press, 1957).

For as the heavens are higher than the earth, so are my ways higher than your ways and my thoughts than your thoughts."[23] The Christian, therefore, does not demand that God change the circumstances of his life to suit his will. He pours out his heart to God and makes known his fear of death and his desire for health. But he concludes his petition with the words of Jesus, "Not my will but thine be done."

The magical healer will propose to bring health through his own cleverness. He will not use hospitals or any of the healing arts which men have found and developed. If he calls upon God at all, it will be in terms of an ultimatum. One magical healer said in a "faith healing" meeting: "If you want health from God, you ask it, and God *will* give it." There was no sense of surrender, no tone of submission to God, and no humility in the statement.

The second distinction between types of faith healing is the interpretation that the healer gives to the fact of death. The faith healer who denies, distorts, or glosses over the fact of physical death does his healing on the basis of unreality. Wayne Oates points out in *Healing: Human and Divine* that such a distortion of reality is the seed bed of neuroses.[24] The patient is persuaded that he is exempt from the laws of nature, that he can be the divine exception, and that circumstances can be changed at his pleasure.

This magical thinking is directly opposed to the biblical accounts of healing. Before Jesus raised Lazarus from the dead, it is made plain, Lazarus was physically dead. First, Jesus told his disciples: "Lazarus is dead."[25] Second, Martha objected: "Lord, by this time there will be an odor, for he has been dead four days."[26]

In the Christian faith, healings are only for a period of time. The minister finally officiates at both the doctor's successes and his failures and maybe for the doctor himself, if the minister should outlive the doctor. The Christian healer is also aware that some people decide to die. A person may be reasonably

[23] Isa. 55:8–9.
[24] p. 235.
[25] John 11:14.
[26] John 11:39.

healthy physically and yet be spiritually empty. This is why Christianity has always stressed the meaning of life rather than the length of life. The Bible reckons life and death in terms of spiritual rebirth. A man who is "in Christ" is alive. One who is not is already dead in his sins.

The nurse should also observe whether or not the healer is a part of a larger community of faith. The charlatan, the magical healer, dwells in isolation. All power depends upon him. But the healer who is true to the biblical examples of healing will be part of a concerned community. In earliest days the Christian faith was conceived to be a healing religion because the Christians rallied round those who were sick. This is well illustrated in James 5:14–16:

> Is any among you sick? Let him call for the elders of the church, and let them pray over him, anointing him with oil in the name of the Lord; and the prayer of faith will save the sick man, and the Lord will raise him up; and if he has committed sins, he will be forgiven. Therefore confess your sins to one another, and pray for one another, that you may be healed. The prayer of a righteous man has great power in its effects.

The person who is spiritually healed may often be one who has been delivered from social isolation or estrangement to a brotherhood in which he is accepted for himself. His suffering is identified with that of others.

Faith and healing also involves nurses and physicians in two ethical problems.[27] One is the responsibility of receiving an accurate diagnosis of illness and exhausting all known procedures for therapy. This is an act of faith in itself. A patient may say to a nurse, "I don't really know what is wrong with me. I hope that the doctor can find out, but I am just trusting in the will of God." The nurse may reply, "Well, Mrs. Johnson, I think that you are already doing God's will by trusting in the diagnosticians to find the cause of your difficulty. I know that you also have in mind your personal faith in God, but I want to assure you that I be-

---

[27] Doniger, *op. cit.*, pp. 250 ff.

lieve you are already doing that which is within his will."

The second ethical issue for nurses and doctors concerns the responsibility of the therapist for the safety and well being of the patient. The patient is putting his faith in the hospital personnel; discharging this trust is a heavy responsibility for them. Both nurses and doctors can testify to the encouraging results that often come when a patient has faith in the healing team of a hospital. If a newly admitted patient asks a nurse if the surgeon whom she has retained is trustworthy, the nurse is promoting true faith healing when she can honestly reply, "You can have faith in Dr. Abel. Whatever questions you have, do not hesitate to mention them to him. The fact that he is on the staff of this hospital indicates that he is a competent surgeon." It is quite a dilemma, of course, when the doctor is not well thought of by either patient or nurse.

In summary, we might ask, "Is faith healing real today?" If only one miracle occurs in a year, it is still a miracle. It may also be true that God chooses today to work his miracles through penicillin and cardiac surgery, with men as his selected media. The greatest of all the miracles of today occurs when a sufferer recognizes that his illness has brought him to a realization of his kinship with Christ and his utter dependence upon God.

4. The Problem of Suffering

PAIN AND SUFFERING are problems that confront both patients and nurses. The sick one's question, "Why does God let me suffer?" challenges everyone who hears it to consider its meaning. Student nurses asked more questions about the meaning of suffering than they did about any other clinical problem in religion and nursing.

There is no one complete, satisfying answer to the problem of suffering. It is one of the great mysteries of mankind. We can only "touch the hem of the garment" which envelops this question. But in the discussion which follows, at least three things can be said: (1) Pain and suffering are a part of a complex, psychophysiological process, (2) suffering can have a redemptive purpose, and (3) the personal attitudes of a nurse are of great importance to patients during suffering.

The Personal Quality of Suffering

The perception of pain varies with individuals. Also, within one person emotional and physical changes will vary the susceptibility to pain. Dr. W. K. Livingston has stated that a painful sensation of unknown origin may be associated with the patient's having the fear of death or cancer. The pain then becomes unbearable. But when convincing evidence to the contrary is offered by the physician, the painful sensation may be immediately reduced.[1]

[1] *Pain Mechanisms* (New York: The Macmillan Company, 1943), p. 64.

The personal elements in pain are also clearly seen in terminal malignancies. In "Psychological Aspects in Terminal Malignancies," Dr. V. R. Zarling has stated that pain and death are the two psychological factors in intractable pain.[2] The basic problem in prolonged pain is the management of fear. In addition, patients may become depressed, react with feelings of guilt and hostility, or show anxiety through restlessness, persistent dread, and uneasiness.

Physiological aspects of pain must be considered along with those that are psychological. Many doctors, such as Dr. Livingston and Dr. Walter Alvarez, have warned against the indiscriminate use of the term "psychic." The distress may come from a disease of physical origin which has not yet been diagnosed. Also, a patient's attitude will vary with the physiological intensity of pain. Dr. Schiffrin distinguishes between four types of pain:

(1) Overwhelming pain, which seems to spread over the entire body. The patient may scream, thrash about on the bed, and utter groans from the depths of his being. He is not influenced by his surroundings.

(2) Severe pain. This is vaguely localized. The patient often seeks to withdraw from everyone. Loud noises and bright lights cause distress.

(3) Moderate pain. The patient is able to localize the pain. His immediate impulse is to fight or flee the stabbing, itching, burning, or tearing sensations that he feels.

(4) Mild pain. This can be localized. The patient is well aware of his surroundings.

It is obvious that the nurse's ministry to the patient will vary with each of these four categories. A smile with pleasant conversation may be a medicine for the soul of a patient who is in mild pain, but it would be very inappropriate to sweetly ask, "How do

---

[2] M. J. Schiffrin, ed., *The Management of Pain in Cancer* (Chicago: Yearbook Publishers, 1956), p. 194.

you feel today?" of a patient who thrashes wildly in bed as pain overwhelms him. His misery is obvious.

What are some of the implications of suffering, this complex psychophysiological process, for religion and nursing?

First, it is helpful for the nurse to be acquainted with Christian and medical teaching to the effect that all aspects of personality are interrelated. Somatic factors will affect the emotions, and vice versa. It is expected, therefore, that the patient's outlook on life will be affected by pain. On the fourth day after an operation, for example, a patient may become quite depressed because the psychological defenses which he had mobilized while facing the operation are spent. The fears which he has repressed may now emerge, and he wonders how it was possible for him to have survived such an ordeal. In such a situation, after reflection, the patient may say to a nurse, "I feel so blue today. I ought to be grateful for all that has happened, but—I just don't know how I will make it." The nurse who is aware of the intimate connection between pain and personality can reply, "You have been through a crisis that took a great deal out of you. You stood the operation well, and you are progressing well, as Dr. C. says. And now you have more time to think. I hope you will tell Dr. C. how you feel, for he expects reactions like this."

If the patient replies, "Well, I certainly do need some inner strength, because I feel weak as water," the nurse might take the Bible from the patient's bedside table and open it to this passage as she offers it to him: "He (God) gives power to the faint, and to him who has no might he increases strength. Even youths shall faint and be weary, and young men shall fall exhausted; but they who wait for the Lord shall renew their strength, they shall mount up with wings like eagles, they shall run and not be weary, they shall walk and not faint." [3] If she has the time to do it, she may read the passage to him.

A person's philosophy of life is another facet of suffering. The one who has been in pain for a long time may feel socially isolated. He may come to believe that no one really cares how much

---

[3] Isa. 40:29–31.

he suffers. This is one of the tragic risks of prolonged pain. A patient may express this feeling to the nurse by saying, "No one can really understand. I wonder why God does not hear me. I feel that I am completely deserted." The nurse might reply, "I imagine that you feel like a man in the Bible who had suffered pain for a long time. If you will allow me to look up the Psalm, I believe that it will say something to you." If the patient nods his head in affirmation, the nurse can read Psalm 77:7–10. Then she may comment, "This man said that it was his own grief, pain, and weakness that caused him to feel that he was all by himself and that God had forgotten him. But God was still with him." It might be well to leave the Bible open by the patient, for the remaining verses of that Psalm state the affirmation of faith which comes to a person after he gives voice to his doubts.

If the patient has spoken earlier of his church and said, "They are praying for me," the nurse can remind him in a moment of loneliness that many friends are remembering him daily. Perhaps the whole church, assembled together on Sunday, mentions him by name.

In these examples the nurse has used the patient's philosophy of life to combat the isolating influences of prolonged pain. One patient was reminded that God loved him and understood his loneliness, while another was taught anew that the church is a fellowship in which suffering is accepted and made endurable through prayer.

In *How Long the Night*[4] Claribel Dick has written of the faith in God that sustained her after an accident. Her love for her husband and children and the skill and courage of her doctor brought her through a long trial of suffering to healing. It is the kind of book that would inspire a patient during convalescence.

The nurse's own philosophy of life is another healing influence. In each instance above, the nurse did not condemn the patient for lacking spiritual strength, nor did she disregard and make light of the anxiety or terror that was creeping into the patient's soul. But a nurse cannot speak this way unless she has thought out her

---

[4] Philadelphia: Judson Press, 1955.

own philosophy of suffering. As has already been said, no neat and final answers to this great mystery can be stated. The least that can be done is to examine some of the biblical interpretations of suffering and apply them to the patient's need.

The Biblical Interpretation of Suffering

The biblical emphasis in this area is not upon an explanation of pain and suffering but upon the strength God can give men to live with and through times of trial. References to suffering are found throughout the Bible, but there is no one coherent, consistent doctrine. The distinctive Christian contribution to the problem of suffering is the revelation, first to the prophets and then in Jesus, that God suffers with men.

In the Old Testament there is no consistent distinction between physical and mental suffering. Psalms 6, 32, and 38 describe physical phenomena such as the wasting away of the body, the festering of wounds, and the loins filled with burning. In these same Psalms there is also a cry for God's forgiveness: "For I am ready to fall, and my pain is ever with me. I confess my iniquity, I am sorry for my sin."[5] The disease, or any other misfortune, was regarded as a manifestation of evil in the soul. Personal suffering was considered a deserved punishment for sin.

In biblical accounts an entire city or nation might suffer physical disaster because of sin. The book of Amos promised the destruction of a heathen nation such as Moab. The prophet also warned Israel, whom God had known of all the families of the earth, that drought and pestilence would follow wilful transgression of his law.

There are passages in the Old Testament which do not substantiate this view of personal retribution. Elihu, in the book of Job, argued for suffering as a discipline or education. Psalm 107 describes trials such as sickness and imprisonment as occasions which turn the thoughts of men toward God. Not just personal suffering but also national catastrophe was presented in the Old Testament as turning the hearts of men toward the Lord. The

---

[5] Psalm 38:17–18.

books of Isaiah and Daniel look beyond the destruction of earthly kingdoms to the coming righteousness of the kingdom of God upon earth.

Suffering may teach men some specific truth. Psalm 73 describes a man who was envious of the arrogant and embittered by the success of proud men. But when his "feet had almost stumbled" he realized, "My flesh and heart may fail, but God is the strength of my heart and my portion forever." [6] Again, in the midst of Hosea's suffering as a betrayed husband, God spoke of Israel's betrayal of their trust with him. Though God had called them as sons, taken them in his arms, and bent down to feed them, they turned from him. But despite their iniquity, the steadfast love of the Lord remained constant toward those who would repent and turn to him. Through their own suffering the psalmist and Hosea received a new truth from God.

The Old Testament teaching which is most akin to the New Testament may be found in Isaiah. God is likened to a shepherd who will feed his flock. He will blot out transgressions for the sake of his own name. He can no more forget his people than a woman can forget her young child. The Servant of God will bear the sorrows and transgressions of men.[7]

It is in passages like these that suffering becomes an occasion when God identifies himself with men. Because they are his creation whom he loves, he suffers with them and provides a means for their redemption.

The means of this redemption was dimly perceived in the book of Isaiah as the Suffering Servant of the Lord. The disciples of Christ saw what the prophets had longed to see and did not see—Jesus, the Son of God. He became the servant of God whose life, death, and resurrection brought redemption to mankind.[8]

The cross of Christ is the distinctive contribution of the New Testament to the problem of suffering. Christ suffered to the death for our redemption. He was the God-man who both understood man's weaknesses and triumphed over them. It is

---

[6] Psalm 73:26.

[7] Isa. 40:11; 43:25; 49:14–15; 53:4–6.

[8] Phil. 2:5–11.

through his example upon earth and his Spirit living within that men can triumph over human suffering.[9]

The New Testament also gives a more complete understanding of the relationship between sin and suffering. Because some Old Testament passages spoke of suffering as a result of sin, many Jews concluded that all suffering was the result of sin. There are many Christians who believe the same thing today. But Jesus taught something different. Speaking of the tower of Silom, which fell and killed eighteen people, Jesus remarked, "Do you think that they were worse offenders than all the others who dwelt in Jerusalem? I tell you, No; but unless you repent you will all likewise perish." [10] When the disciples asked whether a man who was born blind was being punished for his sin or his parents', Jesus answered, "It was not that this man sinned, or his parents, but that the works of God might be made manifest in him." [11] In the Sermon on the Mount, Jesus said that the sun rises upon evil and good and rain falls upon the just and unjust.[12] In all these ways he was saying that sin results in suffering, but all suffering is not necessarily the result of sin. In the first century many persons identified physical catastrophe with God's judgment, as they do in the twentieth century. Jesus specifically rejected this view.

The apostle Paul also spoke of suffering. He found that his own "thorn in the flesh" was a constant reminder of his human limitations. It kept him humble.[13] He found that the suffering of a Christian can produce character when it is accepted with a godly spirit.[14]

The inevitable pain and suffering that is a part of human experience was not ignored in the Bible just because it was not explained. Instead, the Christian receives power from God through the example and the Spirit of Christ by which he may triumph even over death. The aim of the Christian life is not to abolish physical death or ignore human suffering but to eliminate that which is cruel, barbarous, and useless. Through resources that

---

[9] Luke 22:42–44; 2 Cor. 4–5; Gal. 1:4; Heb. 4:14–16.
[10] Luke 13:4–5.
[11] John 9:3.
[12] Matt. 5:45.
[13] 2 Cor. 12:7–10.
[14] Rom. 5:1–5.

come from beyond themselves, some suffering can be elevated and sublimated to make men humane, stimulating, unselfish, and creative.

The Burden and the Cross

Caution is necessary in attributing creative qualities to suffering. There is some pain and suffering that is senseless, inhuman, and meaningless. The martyrs slain for their faith cried out, "O Sovereign Lord, holy and true, how long before thou wilt judge and avenge our blood on those who dwell upon the earth?"[15] "How long, O Lord?" may be our cry in the face of some forms of suffering. There is nothing sublime about a four-year-old child's dying of rabies or a Negro accident victim's writhing in the emergency room while the administration tries to decide where to put him in an "all white" hospital.

The Christian must discriminate between the kinds of suffering. One way to do this is to ask questions such as: (1) Is this suffering necessary? (2) Is it voluntary? (3) For what shall we suffer?

In answer to the first question, people bear pain with more courage when it seems to be necessary. In fact, as has been pointed out earlier in this chapter, an explanation as to the source and meaning of pain can cause it to diminish rapidly.[16] Patients will move a limb under medical direction despite great pain when there is hope that this activity will lead to better functioning of the affected part. It is important that a patient understand that pain may be a part of his hospital experience. If the doctor has explained this to the patient, the nurse's task is made easier when she reinterprets pain and discomfort as an inevitable part of healing.

"Inevitable" is used here deliberately and cautiously. What seems a necessary pain today may be largely alleviated in the future. Four generations ago physicians and clergymen looked with disfavor upon the use of anesthesia during childbirth. They regarded pain in childbirth as a natural process that women must bear as the result of sin.

People seem to suffer most when pain seems to them to be un-

---

[15] Rev. 6:10.

[16] See p. 70.

necessary. This is often the mood behind the continual question of patients, "Why did this happen to me?" Many patients as well as nurses adjust themselves to the fact of unexplainable suffering by saying, "It is the will of God." With this phrase people may mean that men are created with human limitations. God does not promise immunity from suffering and death. They may mean that God has received in love a departed saint who trusted in him, and that Christians can trust God even though they do not understand all the mysteries of life. If this is the meaning, it would be acceptable to the Christian. Some other implications of such phrases as, "God took this child home because he needed another baby" are to be questioned. Suffering is not absolutely inevitable and unchangeable. God does not ordain this particular pain. This man is not necessarily being punished by God for his sins.

The chaplain or pastor usually talks over with a patient the meaning of God's will for him. But when a nurse is asked, she may respond by saying, "We do not understand all the mysteries of life or the necessity of some suffering, and yet we trust in God's loving concern for us in the midst of all these things."

The second question that suffering raises is, "Is it voluntary?" This is where a distinction must be made between a burden and a cross. A Christian takes up his cross. It is self-chosen. A burden, on the other hand, is imposed by circumstances. This difference is made most specific in the first letter of Peter. If a Christian is punished for what is wrong, the suffering that results from it should not be considered to be a "cross." [17] But if a Christian experiences trials for "righteousness' sake," he will be blessed.[18] The Christian is to rejoice "in so far as you suffer Christ's sufferings." [19]

These qualifying phrases are very important, especially in our modern day when we have learned so much about the unconscious satisfactions which some people derive from their suffering. One mother flew five hundred miles to be at the bedside of her married son as soon as she heard that he was to have an appendectomy, although neither the son nor his wife had requested

[17] 1 Peter 2:14.
[18] 1 Peter 3:14.
[19] 1 Peter 4:13.

her to come. After the operation the doctor assured her that her son was not in danger. But the mother would tell the nurses, the attendants, the doctors, and the chaplains about her great anxieties. She spoke of all her "sufferings" for the sake of her son. If she was encouraged—and a few moments listening has all the encouragement she needed—she began to insinuate that the young wife was not caring for her boy as he was cared for "back home."

The nurses observed that this mother's anxiety was out of proportion to the occasion. There seemed to be some underlying struggle which was hinted at by her hostility toward her daughter-in-law and her possessive attitude toward the son. There was no doubt that this poor woman was suffering, but did she know why she was suffering? In vain the nurse reassured her that her son was all right. The nurse meant that he was a healthy young man who was normally recovering from an operation and was being cheered by the presence of his wife and thoughts of his children. But to the mother it could never be "all right" for her boy to have left home. His sickness confirmed her fears that he would not do well when he was no longer under her protection.

From a Christian point of view, the mother's attitude was inappropriate because she tried to make a cross out of a burden. It is natural for a man to leave his father and mother and cleave to his wife. At the same time, it is normal for a mother to show concern for her son and long to be with him. These are some of the creative anxieties of growing families. But the mother in the example above made these natural concerns into something unusual. Her suffering was out of proportion to the immediate stress. Martyrdom was the overtone of her conduct, but a Christian is not a martyr unless he suffers for Christ.

The same distinction may be applied when a person seeks to atone for unconscious guilt by physical suffering. In *Nervous Indigestion and Pain* [20] Dr. Walter Alvarez notes that some patients seemed to welcome operations or painful procedures as a physical compensation for their problem. The patient appears to

---

[20] New York: Harper & Brothers, 1954.

"hang on" to the pain. Perhaps he is thinking, "If I suffer a little outwardly, it will take away my inner guilt."

Sometimes the outer suffering is used as a justification for an inner, unresolved conflict. One woman spoke critically of the nurses to the chaplain, of one chaplain to another one, the nurse to a doctor, and the doctor to the administrator. She continually related how she was mistreated by members of her family. When a visitor asked her how she could live with such feelings of persecution and resentment, she replied, "But you don't know what pain I have to endure. I simply cannot sleep because of these horrible cramps and headaches. My husband does not sympathize. My doctor does not understand. The nurses ignore me. Only God can help me. Will you pray?" She regarded her physical suffering as a cross which she had to bear when actually she was burdened with hostility.

At times the distinction between a cross and a burden may be obliterated. The wife of an invalid husband may carry both a cross and a burden. The invalidism of her husband is her burden. The couple consciously declared at marriage that they would stay by each other in sickness and in health. It is her attitude toward herself and her husband that relates to the cross. In the factory where she sought employment to support her family there were men who offered to "take her out for a good time." She refused these requests and continued to work with these men even though she longed for physical affection. This was a cross which "tests the genuineness of her faith." [21] Some of the women in her neighborhood or at work tried to work out their own problems through hers. They bluntly inquired about her personal life and insinuated that she brought this on herself. One said, "I don't know how you stand it, dearie. I almost went crazy before my husband died. If I were you, I would put him away somewhere." For the wife to understand the unresolved difficulties in those who make such suggestions and to turn them aside with a soft answer was a cross heavy for her to bear. They were tempting her with some of the attitudes which she had to

[21] 1 Peter 1:6–7.

overcome almost daily. It is at a time like this that she was in great need of a Christian fellowship, a group of people who understood her trial and strengthened her by bringing out the best that human love can give.[22]

When a person bears a cross, he is suffering for the sake of a way of life that he has voluntarily accepted; it is a conscious reaction to a known cause. That cause must be directly related to Christian values.

Christian values in suffering raise a third question: "For what shall we suffer?" Some people live as though their purpose in life was to avoid suffering. A nurse soon discovers that some pain in this life is inevitable. The problem is to find some way to live despite insecurity and frustration. In the Hebrew-Christian tradition, suffering is not removed but redeemed. The Christian has something worth living and dying for.

One of the goals of life is personal growth. Some suffering is a part of development from childhood to manhood. As Professor Peter Bertocci has written, there must be insecurity in a person's life in order that he may learn the meaning of forgiving love.[23] The child who is always "loved," in the sense that his every desire is gratified by his parents, does not become a loving person. He orients his life about self-satisfaction. On the other hand, the child who is frustrated in his attempts to satisfy only himself can grow. He learns that other people have rights, feelings, and privileges of their own. People are not things to be used; they are persons to be respected. By the correction of his parents and the self-discipline of shame and guilt, the child learns that love cannot be taken for granted. Some suffering, some restraint, is necessary if he is to become a lovable being. Furthermore, as the young person learns to control his own impulses he finds that it is as desirable to love as to be loved. He begins to give himself to others, just as his parents gave themselves to him.

With this personal background, a person can accept God as a just and loving Father. He does not expect God to change all

---

[22] 1 Peter 5:9.

[23] *Religion as Creative Insecurity* (New York: Association Press, 1958) pp. 55 ff.

conditions to meet his personal convenience. His discipline in childhood has prepared him to receive some suffering as the price of spiritual growth. Life has not been built about self-satisfaction but about self-transcendent goals.

The Patient's Expectation of the Nurse

In a hospital suffering involves not only the patient but also the hospital personnel. The nurse may go back to her room and think about the meaning of suffering after she has seen a person in great pain. She is personally affected, but she must react to it with confidence and serenity. She must see the patient through the eyes of a nurse. Her professional role is of great importance to the suffering person.

The nurse's professional role with a patient in pain is akin to a mother's relationship to her child. This was one conclusion of Dr. Beatrix Cobb's study of nurse-patient relationships.[24] When fifty patients hospitalized for a serious chronic disease were asked for the ingredients of good nurse-patient relationships, they suggested four major qualities: (1) the nurse should have an attitude of empathy more than of sympathy; (2) the personality of the nurse must be one of warmth and cheerfulness; (3) conversation between the patient and the nurse must be free and easy, and her general attitude must be warm and reassuring; and (4) promptness is an outstanding virtue.

By empathy, the patients meant that the nurse should be able to identify herself with the patient's dilemma without too much pity. She should treat each patient as she would like to be treated. Empathy comes through both experience and careful thought concerning the questions that have already been raised in this chapter. Unless the nurse can achieve objectivity by relating the suffering of the patient to some of the issues that have been discussed, she may find herself demoralizing both the patient and herself with too much sympathy.

The patients' second expectation of the nurse concerned her personality. Warmth and cheerfulness were stressed by the pa-

[24] "Nurse-Patient Relationship," *Journal of the American Geriatrics Society*, IV (July, 1956), 690–98.

tients. They asked that the nurse realize that their crankiness may be due to pain or fear. They suggested that she overlook a few faults. Perhaps the nurse's understanding of the discussion of the tragic prestige of pain may help her in some of these situations. In addition, patients expressed the wish that the nurse be impartial, "be kind and treat all alike." This desire reminds the nurse that she belongs to *all* the patients and cannot work out her own subjective feelings in special attention to a patient who reminds her of some friend or relative. Since every nurse will meet persons who awaken feelings akin to those felt toward members of her family or toward herself, it is advisable to have some supervisor, chaplain, or friend with whom these feelings may be discussed. The nurse should warn herself by asking, "Why is it that I keep thinking of that one patient after I get off of duty? Is it something about me or some issue I have not faced that brings him to my mind continually?"

Patients also ask for a cheerful personality. They want the nurse to convey a spirit of hope. It is as if on occasion they hunger for laughter and a light spirit. Otherwise, the shadow of suffering or impending death may become too grim. If a nurse has not worked out some of her own convictions about life, death, and suffering, her distress may be so intent that the patient recognizes it. But if the nurse has considered suffering as a burden to be borne, she will carry this attitude with her to her patients. The way in which she finds meaning in the face of disease which neither she nor the doctor can conquer will be an example of strength to a patient who must face it personally.

This expectation relates both to the verbal and nonverbal communication of the nurse. She *may* think of one of the Scripture passages or replies which have been stated in this chapter, or she may not. She should not despair because she cannot remember these things, for her attitude may convey much more than words. If she makes a patient feel that he is getting individual attention, if she thinks of reasons why he is irritable and shows an understanding attitude through both her manner and her voice, she will be helpful to the sick one.

The patients also spoke of the great need for promptness when they were in great pain. If a nurse does not care to look upon suffering, or if she sees the approach of death as a brutal stranger to her way of life, she may not promptly answer the patient's call. She may busy herself with so many routine duties that she "does not hear the bell." When the patient signals for attention, she may neglect the patient and excuse herself by saying, "I forgot about him."

It is evident, therefore, that the experience of pain and suffering is a personal matter for both the patient and the nurse. The nurse will not find all the answers to this great mystery in this book or in her lifetime. But she can deepen and widen the horizons of her life through the resources suggested in this chapter, through the example and counsel of her friends and teachers, and by a resolute examination of her own feelings.

What the nurse *does* for a suffering patient is important, but what she *is* can be the basic source of a sick person's comfort and strength.

For Further Reading:

The nurse will be aided in her understanding of suffering through an exploration of the following books:

BERTOCCI, PETER S. *Religion as Creative Insecurity*. New York: Association Press, 1958.

BRYDEN, JAMES. *Letters to Mark, On God's Relation to Human Suffering*. New York: Harper & Brothers, 1953.

CABOT, RICHARD, AND DICKS, RUSSELL. *The Art of Ministering to the Sick*. New York: The Macmillan Company, 1945, chapters V–VIII.

FOSDICK, H. E. "High Uses of Trouble," "When God Lets Us Down," and "Six Paradoxes Concerning Trouble," in *The Secret of Victorious Living* (New York: Harper & Brothers, 1934) and *Successful Christian Living* (New York: Harper & Brothers, 1937).

FRANKL, VIKTOR. *The Doctor and the Soul*. New York: Alfred Knopf, 1955.

LUTHER, MARTIN. *Letters of Spiritual Counsel*. Philadelphia: Westminster Press, 1956.

The nurse can suggest the following reading to patients:

DICK, CLARIBEL F. *How Long the Night*. Philadelphia: Judson Press, 1955.
DICKS, RUSSELL. *My Faith Looks Up*. Philadelphia: Westminster Press, 1949.
OATES, WAYNE. *Grace Sufficient*. Nashville: Broadman Press, 1951.
———. *The Revelation of God in Human Suffering*. Philadelphia: Westminster Press, 1959.
SCHERZER, CARL. *Springs of Living Water*. Philadelphia: Westminster Press, 1951.

5. Guilt and Forgiveness

IN THE PREVIOUS CHAPTER it was pointed out that Jesus specifically denied the false idea that all suffering is the result of personal sin. People suffer as a result of sin, but this does not always come in the form of a physical disease.

There are many occasions when patients ask, "Why does God allow me to suffer like this?" One of these occasions was reported by a student nurse as follows:

Mr. W. was admitted for surgery. He realized the necessity of the operation since without surgery he would probably lose his left leg. He appeared resigned to the fact and fairly cheerful before surgery. The operation was performed, and he took the procedure well and recovered quite rapidly. Six days later he was discharged from the hospital in an apparently satisfactory condition.

About a month later I noticed that he was readmitted to the surgical division I was working on. I entered the room with a cheerful hello, and Mr. W. appeared very pleased to see me again. He seemed, however, very worried and apprehensive. He stated that he was here to have the same operation over again due to an infection of the graft, which would have to be removed. I commented how beautifully he recovered from the other operation and that he would surely do as well this time. His attitude had changed completely. He explained the great financial burden this would be on his family, since he had been unable to work for such a long period of time. There was no telling when he would again be able to return to his job. He asked, "Why is it something like this must happen to me? Isn't it enough for things to go wrong once? God must think I deserve more punishment."

I tried to encourage him and explain that this was only an unfortunate incident and not intended as punishment. He finally agreed to this but remained extremely concerned about his wife and children. He said that lately he had enough financial problems without the great expense of two operations. I managed to change the conversation to sports since he was a great football fan, as I remembered from before.

When I left the room, he seemed somewhat more cheerful and less anxious about his problems—at least for a while anyway.

At other times a nurse might respond to a patient's question about suffering and sin by saying, "You have had to bear pain so long that I can understand why you would wonder about God." The patient may then go on to reassert his faith in God but at the same time explain that he does not understand why this should happen to him when he has lived such a good life, has much business to complete, etc. Under these conditions, the patient is discovering that he is not the divine exception. The nurse may help him to see this by replying, "I don't think that God *sends* sickness upon us, but I do believe that he permits us to undergo the same amount of suffering and grief as any other human being."

When patients discuss the relationship between sin and suffering, it is important to know the amount of personal responsibility which they feel for their condition. The nurse might ask, "Do you mean that this sickness is something for which you feel personally responsible?" A woman who had many family duties replied to a similar question, "Well, I don't know that I *did* anything to deserve this. When I asked why God let this happen to me, I meant that this shouldn't happen to me because I should be taking care of the children and all those things. But—my husband assures me that they are doing well." In this case, the woman seemed to be more concerned about her general responsibility to her family than she was about personal responsibility for her illness. Strong feelings of guilt were not evident in her response.

But another person may give an answer that closely connects sin and suffering. Sometimes suffering results from some objective sin. The driver of a car which ran off the road at high speed may feel personally responsible for the dire effects of the accident upon the occupants of the car. Perhaps he is right. His own injuries may worry him much less than the sorrow he has brought to others. He needs an opportunity to talk about this, not only to his nurse and doctor, but also to his pastor or chaplain. The nurse who says, "Oh, now, you mustn't feel bad about that," is simply refusing to accept the patient's feeling.

Relatives, as well as patients, often feel personally responsible for suffering. The parent of a hospitalized child lamented, "Oh, if we had just paid attention to his complaints yesterday, if we had just thought what his headache meant, he wouldn't be in such terrible condition now!" When people are distraught with guilt, it is imperative for the nurse to report this to the doctor in order that he may strongly reassure the parents that it is natural for them to feel that way about the child's condition, although they could hardly be expected to diagnose the symptoms of a complicated disease when it was just beginning to emerge.

Some other evidences of personal responsibility for suffering are more difficult to handle because the patient's whole way of life may be involved. The sick one may have little understanding of the connection between sin and his present illness. This type of responsibility may be illustrated from the medical records of a business firm in Houston, Texas. An analysis of the yearly sick reports indicated that 25 per cent of the employees were responsible for 75 per cent of the days lost. It was also discovered that the 25 per cent were sick repeatedly. This was in contrast to the other 75 per cent of the employees, who were usually sick only once. If they were sick more than once, their symptoms tended to recur in the same body system or organ.

What made the difference? The doctors found that the 25 per cent were discontented with life. They were disappointed in their relationships with other people or dissatisfied with their single state or frustrated in their attempts to create a home. There was an element of personal responsibility in their illness.

In such situations it requires the teamwork of the nurse, the doctor, the chaplain, and the social worker to bring their basic dissatisfactions to the attention of these people. Only then can they give up the self-defeating pattern of illness which has been their way of escape from a life that has lost its meaning.

"Worldly" and "Godly" Sorrow

Personal responsibility is one important factor in suffering. Another is pride. A patient may say, "Being in this bed gives me a chance to think of the way I have treated my family. They must think horrible things about me. I know it is wrong, but I can't forgive myself. What can I do?" If the nurse has observed that this is a proud man, she should tread warily. It would be well for her to stop and consider some of the distinctions between "worldly" and "godly" sorrow before she plunges into a deep discussion with this patient.

"Worldly" sorrow is related to self-glory. Some persons are occupied with the urge to lift themselves above others and triumph over an unappreciative world. Jealous feelings and vicious actions may cause great discomfort, but the basic pride cannot be touched. One patient who had been in the hospital several times for vague complaints made continual demands of the nurses and became quite indignant if they did not answer her every request with prompt cheerfulness. She insisted upon more medication than the doctor had ordered, and when this was refused, she began a methodical campaign which went like this: "If the doctor just knew how I suffered, he would give me something. If you would just call him for me, it would relieve my distress."

One morning, after the patient had accused a nurse of being "hard-hearted and unresponsive," the doctor told her he understood exactly why she was suffering. He was not going to order any more medication, no matter how much she tried to wear down the nurses with threats and sympathy. The patient immediately denied that she had any harsh feelings against any nurses. She was so upset by this that she called in one of the nurses as soon as the doctor had left and said, "I know that you girls are the sweetest things on earth. Sometimes you must think that I am being ugly. But if you just *knew* how much I suffer. Even the doctors do not understand."

The woman had been reminded by her physician that she was

a hostile person who would manipulate others for her own ends with any means at her disposal. She could not accept this. Instead, to alleviate her guilt she immediately denied it to both the doctor and the nurses. She tried to "smooth it over" by flattering the nurses and seeking to place blame upon the doctor. She really suffered but would allow no one to touch the unresolved hatred and self-punishment which caused her agony.

The opposite of "worldly grief" is "godly grief."[1] Godly grief is characterized by a concern for persons. First of all, the person who feels godly grief grieves because of what his sin has done to other people. In godly grief an adulterer will be concerned about the hurt he has caused to a wife who loves and trusts him. He will be ashamed to receive the pure affection of his children, who think he is the most wonderful man in the world. He may say little about "the other woman," but he will often think, "How could I have left these people that are so important to me and cheapened myself in this way?" Certainly the man needs to find an answer to that question before his repentance is complete, but at least he is on the right road. In "worldly sorrow," by contrast, the adulterer is filled with anxiety lest he be caught. If he has left a clue unguarded, he is furious with himself for his own stupidity. His overwhelming desire is to keep *himself* from being hurt.

A second characteristic of godly sorrow is a sense of shame. Since he has outraged God's love, the sinner is more embarrassed before his Heavenly Father than he is afraid. This is to be distinguished from worldly sorrow, which is characterized by a belief that God will punish unmercifully. In fear the guilty man makes ready his excuses and denials. He is not openly ashamed for his sin.

In godly grief the sinner is concerned about what he has done to God. He knows that God loves him and believes that God is hurt because he has deliberately disobeyed. The man looks for no excuse because he has consciously accepted the way of Christ and committed himself to God's will. In addition, excuses

---

[1] 2 Cor. 7.

would simply push him further away from God. Instead, he repents and desires the restoration of his fellowship with God. This longing is as natural as the desire to renew fellowship with any others whom he might have wronged. David expressed this truth when he said, "Against thee, thee only, have I sinned, and done that which is evil in thy sight."[2] This psalm was presumably written after David had committed adultery with Bathsheba. He had sinned against her and had broken trust with the nation. But most of all, David felt a deep alienation from the God who had brought him to the kingdom and to a successful reign. Because he had depended most upon him, God was the one whom he felt that he had betrayed in the greatest degree.

The Judgment and Mercy of God

God is more eager to hear confession than men are inclined to utter it. He is more able to forgive than men are prone to forgive themselves. Nurses can suggest this fact to patients whose sorrow has the marks of "godly grief."

The godly person feels that there is no health in him before God. He longs for any forgiveness. This is matchlessly portrayed in Jesus' conversation with Simon the Pharisee about the woman who poured ointment on the Lord's feet.[3]

God judges us in order that he may lead us to repentance and newness of life. If we know that a person understands the deepest sins of our life, his acceptance of us *in spite of* these things will have deep meaning for us. An elderly woman said, "Nurse, I often have the most terrible fears. I just don't think that I am ready to die." If the nurse says, "Oh, now, you are one of the sweetest patients we have ever had. I *know* that you have nothing to be afraid of. Now don't you ever think of that again," she has given an easy answer but has not permitted the woman to explain why she is afraid. She has not accepted the depth of the patient's stress. On the other hand, if she is willing to walk into the valley of the shadow of fear of death with the patient, she may bring great comfort. The nurse might say, "Well, I

---

[2] Psalm 51:4.

[3] Luke 7:36–50.

know that there is a fear of dying, but I don't know if that's the fear of which you speak or not." Thus the patient is permitted to talk about her feeling in an atmosphere of understanding. Perhaps she fears death itself, but she may be more afraid of her repressed negative feelings such as hostility or guilt.

Just as the depth of acceptance gives meaning to a nurse's relationship with patients, so the judgment of God makes the realization of forgiveness more meaningful. When a man feels that God knows *all* about him and still receives him with grace, his fears on that score will be dissipated. God knows him better than any other person. It is almost humorous to read Martin Luther's conversations with the devil when the latter accused Luther of various sins. In his later years Luther replied, "Why, yes, Devil, I know about these, and here, let me add a few that you have missed." Luther knew that God had accepted him by faith alone. It was not his works or his righteousness that had earned him his salvation.

This personal relationship of trust and understanding between man and God distinguishes godly sorrow and God's forgiveness from worldly sorrow and the incomplete forgiveness of men. In godly grief the sinner becomes conscious that he has wounded the love of God. At the same time, he finds that God has already forgiven him for this wrong, because God's love for man overcomes the suffering which he has endured from the faithlessness of men. God does not stand before a cosmic scale and balance good deeds against evil ones. Instead, he is portrayed by Jesus as a father who sees his son while he is a great way off, runs to meet him, and rejoices that his son who was lost has now been found.

For Further Reading:

Oates, Wayne. *Anxiety and Christian Experience.* Philadelphia: Westminster Press, 1955, chapter IV.

Sherrill, Lewis J. *Guilt and Redemption.* Richmond: John Knox Press, 1945.

6. Depression and Doubt

Depression

THIS CHAPTER ON DEPRESSION follows logically because depression may be one of the symptoms of guilt.

Both guilt and its resulting feelings of depression may result from broken relationships with people who are important in a person's life. Some authorities, such as Lewis Sherrill, explain it this way: When a person has a deep conflict with someone who is significant to him, he gets mad inside himself; then he begins to feel guilty about these hostile thoughts; finally, he punishes himself inwardly: he disparages and depresses himself.[1]

Depression may usually be attributed to one of three causes. The first of these involves inner aggression and unspeakable guilt. A patient deeply resented his father's overbearing and self-righteous attitude. Yet he dared not oppose the parent's wishes. As a result, he was angry with himself and mused, "He shouldn't talk that way to me; I *ought* to do something. Someday I won't take this any longer." Later, however, he was overwhelmed with the thought, "I ought to honor my father and mother. They have been good to me—in their way. I shouldn't think this way about my father, for after all, he's paying my way through school." This answered the problem only for a time. The basic hurt and the resultant hostility were not resolved. Instead, the patient smothered his feeling under a thin blanket of state-

[1] Lewis Sherrill, *Guilt and Redemption* (Richmond: John Knox Press, 1946).

ments which usually began with "I ought to," "I should," or "It is expected."

The hostility had to go somewhere, so it burned through the patient's soul like an underground fire smoldering in a mine. It is no wonder that the patient was depressed. He was like the Spartan youth who hid a fox under his cloak to escape detection. The animal gnawed a hole in him. In like manner, unresolved feelings of resentment can eat holes in the human spirit.

When a vivid reminder of his inner conflicts comes to such a person, a "blue spell" may be the result. One nurse reported that one of her patients was always depressed after a visit from her husband. The patient resented the boyish, irresponsible way in which her husband allowed her to take all the family responsibilities, but she could never say this to him. Similarly, a nurse may feel mean, cross, and tired after a visit to her home. It would be helpful if she would admit to her roommate that she is hard to get along with after such a trip. In time she may begin to ask how her friends get their parents to accept the fact that they're grown up. If she can air some of her feelings without feeling too guilty, she may learn that some rebellion against parents is normal. It is not an unspeakable subject.

The word "unspeakable" is often a bottleneck in the growth process. So long as the person's hostility is directed inwardly, he will suffer the tortures of his own aggression. This way of thinking is one cause of depression. It is characterized by broken relationships with important persons and results in unexpressed, unresolved hostility. There seems to be no external cause, so it is called "autonomous" depression.

Depression may also result from more obvious causes, such as the death of a loved one, the loss of a part of the body in surgery, a sudden business catastrophe, a move to a new and strange community, an aftermath of critical operations, or the removal of a loved one to a mental hospital, tuberculosis hospital, or any other institution for a long period of time. This second type of depression is termed "reactive," because it is a reaction to severe loss or personal strain.

A third cause of depression is related to physical aspects of personality. Drs. Davidoff and Russ have described how metabolic disturbances, deficiency states, toxic infections, brain damage, or other disease may lead to depressive symptoms.[2]

All three types of depression probably will require more attention than the nurse can give. Physically induced reactions demand a doctor; reactive depressions, especially after death, call for a minister or other counselor. Each of these authorities should have some specific suggestions for the nurse concerning her personal ministry to the patient.

From a religious point of view, there are two things to know about depression.

First, the normal process of life contains moments as bad as any of those which are usually associated with the psychoses. There are times when social evil descends like smog upon the sensitive Christian. He cannot shake off the weight which depresses his soul when he sees people suffering from injustice, poverty, or entrenched vice. George Fox, founder of the Quakers, had psychotic-like depressions, but they arose out of his compassion for his followers, the Friends, who languished in prison because they were loyal to his teaching. Again, a student nurse told how she would "lose her spirit" whenever her father entertained his friends with cocktails at home. "Nothing I said could change him, and I wanted to respect him. I used to cry in my room, but after a while, I got to the place that I lost hope and just went to a friend's house when he brought the liquor home." Although the father knew all the social-climbing arguments for drinking, he finally stopped drinking for this reason: "Anything that makes my daughter feel that way about me has got to go."

Second, Christianity has a place for both the best and the worst in life. This broadness is characterized by faith, even in Psalms that begin in the depths of despair: "Out of the depths I cry to thee, O Lord!" [3] "Save me, O God! For the waters have come up to my neck. I sink in deep mire, where there is no foothold." [4] The Christian is not necessarily the person who has never been

---

[2] Paul Hoch and Joseph Zubin, *Depression* (New York: Grune and Stratton, 1954), pp. 225 ff.

[3] Psalm 130:1.

[4] Psalm 69:1–2.

blue or who is always smiling. He may be like Christian in John Bunyan's *The Pilgrim's Progress*. Both Christian and his companion, Pliable, fell into the slough of Despond. Pliable crawled out the way he came in, on the side leading back to the City of Destruction. Christian waded on through the mire until he came out on the side near the cross.

Christianity does not promise immunity from despair but deliverance.

Doubt

What has just been said of depression may also be said concerning doubt. The Christian is *not* necessarily a person without doubts. The New Testament records the misgivings of the disciples about the resurrection, as well as Peter's blindness to the inevitable suffering which Jesus predicted for himself. Jesus' cry: "My God, my God, why hast thou forsaken me?" [5] is also recorded.

It is normal process of growth for a person to have religious doubts. Peter felt deep remorse and questioned himself after he betrayed his Lord three times. His bitter tears attested his feelings. Judas doubted his Master, also, but betrayed him and hanged himself. The difference is that Peter waited for the resurrection.

This is worth considering about our doubts: They can destroy us if we act only on impulses. But they can lead to the birth of a more mature self if we will have the patience and guidance to work through them.

Doubts are resolved very much as depressions are—by breaking up old patterns of thinking and establishing more satisfying ways through the loving encouragement of people who mean something to us. To see how this works, it is advisable to think of some of the typical religious doubts which may come to student nurses.

First, there are the questions that come as a part of the normal shift from traditional to personal loyalties. On the one hand,

---

[5] Mark 15:34.

young people have questions about their parents' religion, but on the other hand, there is fear that one will "lose everything" if the inquiry into sacred matters goes too deep. This is the risk that every young person must face if the teachings of Christ are to become a personal possession. Some of the emphases of older people will pass away; younger people must determine what is enduring in what they have received. They must pray God to be saved from the impulsive assertion that they are wiser than their fathers as well as the hasty assurance that parents are right in *all* things.[6]

A second type of doubt is closely related to this questioning of traditional loyalties. It is the doubt that symbolizes part of the normal rebellion of adolescents. Unfortunately, rebellion against parents and others is not always resolved into renewed appreciation on both sides. If the basic relationship of parent and child is unhealthy, deep doubts may arise. A young lady who had always been told by her mother that she was "no good" came to her pastor and said, "I long to hear your sermons on how God loves everyone, but I can't bring myself to believe that he loves me." No one had ever thought she was lovable as a child, so she doubted that even God could love her now.

A young person may doubt himself if parents have required that he do and think exactly as they wish in order to receive the reward of their love for him. Superficially, he may think that he has been given much liberty, such as a right to choose his playmates and clothes or the time when he is going to wear a raincoat. But he has never been able to make any basic decisions for himself because he knows he will be rejected if he does. If he wants his parents to come to see him in a school play and they wish to have friends in for dinner that night, he dares not tell them how unhappy he is that they will not support him with their interest. If the parents take many trips without him, he is afraid to assert himself and demand that he go too. In later years this person may

[6] Gordon Allport has an illuminating discussion of this type of doubt among young people in *The Individual and His Religion* (New York: The Macmillan Company, 1950), pp. 99–121.

be cynical and disillusioned. He may look upon religion as a means of manipulating people just as his parents used him for their own convenience.

Religious doubts are often very strong when parents use religion to keep their children obedient to their every whim and prejudice. A young woman had been deeply hurt by a young man with whom she was in love. The quarrel also shattered her hopes that through marriage she would break the tyranny of her mother. Completely shaken by the experience, she wished to consult a psychiatrist, but her mother vehemently opposed this and told her she could "pray it through." The girl asked her pastor what to do and was assured that psychiatric consultation might be helpful. When the daughter used the pastor's opinion in an argument with her mother, the mother's fury knew no bounds. She said, "To think that he would want me to be humiliated in that way! I am your mother, and you are not going to see any doctor about something that I can handle for you with the Lord. If you had faith like I have, you wouldn't need a psychiatrist."

The next night the mother arose during the testimony period in prayer meeting and said that the Lord had given her a great victory. Her daughter had almost given in to the counsel of the world and gone to a psychiatrist. But she had prayed about this and persuaded her daughter to seek God's help instead. The daughter was so humiliated and enraged by her mother that she never went to that church again. Doubt about religion arose out of the mother's misuse of religion.

A third type of doubt may be related to a break in personal relationships. Broken courtships, especially those between persons who have prayed intensely about marriage, may shake their faith. The grief of a broken relationship will be especially severe if the girl or the boy has adopted the idea that two "souls" are destined for each other from eternity. Although there is no Christian foundation for this myth, young men and women often ask God if this is "the one." Actually, there is a good bit of trial and error in the courtship process so that a disruption of plans may be viewed as an opportunity for the young persons to learn something about themselves. The boy may have idealized the girl and smothered any expression of her feelings. He may have self-righteously demanded that she conform to his expectations until she could bear it no longer. If she had the grace and the courage to tell him why she refuses him, he might learn something about his own perfectionism. Similarly, a girl who does whatever a boy wants may find that he tires of her after a time. Trying to find out his wishes may only aggravate the problem. What he really desires is a woman who has a personality of her own. After the engagement is broken she may lament that she tried so hard, but the trouble is that she was trying to be putty in his hands rather than a person to be respected.

This rupture of interpersonal relationships may also lead to doubts when there are clashes between parents and children, husbands and wives, or students and those in authority. One woman told her pastor, "I can't believe that I am a Christian any more, because a Christian wouldn't have the thoughts that I have about my children." She was having continual clashes with her children which greatly increased her anxiety and guilt. As she unfolded the problems of her home life, it became apparent that the father took no responsibility for the children. When the wife was encouraged to take only her part of the load and point out ways in which the husband could assume his responsibilities, the clashes with the children diminished, and the whole family began to come to church.

The loss of a loved one by death is another common source of doubt. Sometimes a nurse may ask a person when he first started having doubts about God. In this situation a man said that it was when his mother died, since "she was the most wonderful person on earth. I can't believe that God would take her away from me." This person had a distorted idea about God; he was also wrestling with the problem of idolatry. He may have worshiped his mother and furiously resented the idea that his idol could be "snatched" from him.

The causes of doubt which have been mentioned thus far are very common and may be a natural part of any life. Some of them are an inevitable result of maturing, such as the shift from traditional to personal loyalties and transient rebellion against parents or other authorities. But there are also causes of doubt which are more difficult to deal with than these.

One of the more entrenched types of doubt arises from extreme dogmatism. This is seen in the person who "protests too much" about everything. The nurse may occasionally meet a patient who has no doubts, no griefs, and no insecurities. If there is any suggestion that the patient is uncomfortable or uneasy about his illness, the idea is quickly repulsed with statements such as, "I thank God that any difficulties I have ever had are always turned to joy. If you will just turn to him yourself, young lady, you'll know that what I say is true. But you don't learn that in most of our churches today." This is a defense against a world that is believed to be hostile. If the unfortunate sufferer would see that there are loving people in the world who will not destroy him if he admits a few mistakes, then he would not have to bristle so much to protect his ego. It is an unhappy dogmatist who says, "Every morning when I wake up and know that I must face the world, I put on my clothes like a suit of armor." He doubts the religion of everyone else until he has carefully examined it because he feels that every man's hand is against him.

Doubt may also be a symptom of a compulsive personality neurosis. One doubt after another and one obsessive curse after another arise to plague the individual. The sufferer may drift about the fringes of the church and occasionally speak of his "mental cancer." He avoids personal contacts because these make him anxious. He cannot go through his rituals if people who may interfere are near.

This form of doubt was recognized in the middle ages as "scrupulosity." Those people came again and again to confess the most trivial errors. They were impelled to return to the priest week after week, fearing they had forgotten to confess a sin. In a modern hospital these persons desire repeated assurance that everything is in order and that they are all right. They may become resentful toward nurses or any others who observe them in their rituals or displace some object which they have carefully laid out. These patients will be as disturbed at the removal of a favorite object from the bedside table as a gangster when his automatic pistol is misplaced. They have made these rituals and objects their protection against a hostile world. If these persons can continue to keep everything in good order, their hidden impulses will not be revealed.

Finally, doubt may be a symptom of the fear of losing control of basic human desires. On occasions this may be a symptom of a neurosis or psychosis. Some neurotic people are afraid that they will slap or make some nasty remark to persons whom they fear. They doubt their ability to act in a socially acceptable manner.

But this form of doubt may also be normal. A girl who has always prided herself on her moral strength may discover that she is not above human weakness. Under the pressure of a final examination she may cheat for the first time; under the spell of an ardent lover she may find herself enjoying things which she had previously condemned in others. Whatever the occasion may be, she may afterwards be overwhelmed with doubts about herself: "How could I do a thing like that?" "What is wrong with me?" The experiences may induce her to re-evaluate her strength and repent of her pride. Then she will become morally stronger than she was before. It is not sinful to be human, or to doubt, or to know personal limitations. Spiritually sensitive people wonder about the great questions of the world and the little questions of their own tomorrows. It is only sinful when individuals will not confide in God and attempt to hide weaknesses from him. It is self-deception to tremble for inner security and at the same time act the part of a self-made man of distinction.

Most of the doubts which we have discussed in this section arise from the normal problems of personal growth and the inevitable reaction to personal crises. Personal growth and spiritual understanding will come to those who endure these uncertainties, seek friendship and counsel, and believe in God's faithfulness.[7]

[7] Heb. 10:32–39; Rom. 1:17.

7. Ministry to the Dying

THE CHRISTIAN is not indifferent about a choice between life and death. He greatly prefers life. Christian people support hospitals because they believe it is God's will to alleviate suffering and restore health.

At the same time, the Christian does not ignore death. Our Lord faced death and swallowed it up in his victory over sin, hell, and the grave.[1] The eternal power of death has been broken. More than that, a follower of Christ has already faced spiritual death in his own life and, though dead in his trespasses, has been made alive in Christ Jesus.[2] The eternal issue has already been settled. If he lives, it is an opportunity for fruitful labor. If he dies, it is an opportunity to be completely with God.[3]

These biblical beliefs were formulated under the threat of martyrdom and the memory of Christ's crucifixion. They were the products of personal experience. They are not fully comprehended in any generation until a person comes face to face with the threat of death. Most people know very little about death until they are confronted by it in the immediate family. People have been protected and sheltered from it. The student nurse may be particularly vulnerable, because soon after she enters nursing school she may watch a patient die; this may be the first time that she has seen a person who was critically ill. But no matter how often a person sees death, it still remains a mystery.

---

[1] 1 Cor. 15:51–58.
[2] Eph. 2:1–10.
[3] Phil. 1:19–26.

There are no easy solutions to the problems connected with death.

The Process of Illness

The process of terminal illness and death must be considered against the background of the healing process. After all, some patients fear that they are going to die when actually they will live. The nurse must therefore know something of the process of illness before she can evaluate death.

Dr. Henry Lederer has described illness in its several stages as a complex psychological situation.[4] The first stage is a period of transition from health to illness. The patient may be anxious about the restriction of his activities and become apprehensive of an unfavorable diagnosis. The nurse may see this reaction in patients who are admitted the night before elective surgery or in medical patients who are just beginning a series of diagnostic tests.

From a religious point of view, the patient is being challenged to make a place for illness in his philosophy of life. To the aggressive, self-made man, sickness just does not fit into his way of living. Illness means passivity; it may also be painful. He has always believed in activity and refused to yield to physical discomfort. But he can no longer be an exception to the ills of the human flesh. He will have to accept some limitations. The nurse may find that such men, or women, are blustery and ill tempered. If a nurse can understand that this is a manifestation of the patient's inner problem, she will not take it personally and can interpret hospital routine with such understanding phrases as: "I know that it is very hard for an active person like you to follow this order, but . . ."

Other patients handle the initial acceptance of illness with passivity. The nurse may be tempted to ignore the seemingly contented patient who lies motionless in bed and asks for nothing. But behind this placid mask may be a seething question: "Can I make a living and keep my place in the family after my arm is

---

[4] "How the Sick View Their World," *Pastoral Psychology*, VIII (May, 1957), 49.

amputated tomorrow?" A few moments in the patient's room and a comment such as the following may meet his need: "Dr. Clark said that he would be by to see you tonight. If you have any questions about the operation, I know that he will be able to help you with them. I think he will understand that you are troubled about it."

The second stage in the experience of illness is the start of therapy and the acceptance of the sickness. The patient now views himself as an ill person. It is at this time that he may regress to a childlike world in which he is egocentric, restricts his interests, and is quite dependent and hypochondriacal. If the nurse frowns, he is worried that she does not like him; if she does not hasten to answer his call, he will condemn her as lazy and uninterested in his welfare. Any gas pain, a different pulse rate, or a muscle tic may become a source of alarm. The events of the world about him have lost their importance. To him, what is *really* important is to know if his temperature is elevated, if his bowel movements are regular, or if his weight has changed for the better.

During illness this regression may be a sign that the patient has redistributed his energies to fight disease. During the most acute stages of illness, therefore, a nurse may be encouraged by these signs of the patient's fight for health. She should not weary him with newspapers, scold him for not going to chapel, or try to tease him into prolonged conversation. Let the patient be sick for a little while. If the nurse has not yet found a place for illness in her philosophy of life, she will not accept this admonition and fight to preserve the illusion of health in the patient at all times. But during the acute stages of sickness, she may have to accept some of *her* limitations just as the patient had to accept some of his at an earlier stage of his illness.

For most patients the restriction of interests during the acute stages of illness is transitory, and the attractions of life reassert themselves as physical health returns. This heralds the third stage of illness, convalescence. In this transitional period from sickness to health the convalescent, like the adolescent, has to leave a protected world. He must "grow up" again and become independent of the kindly attention and protection of nurses and doctors.

This is the time to bring in the newspapers and point out the window to the flowers that bloom in the spring. Weaning the patient from the protective environment of illness calls for a judicious balancing of support and discipline. The nurse can reassure the patient that he can stand on his feet at the same time that she gently urges him to follow the doctor's directions for exercise.

During convalescence the patient needs both inner strength and outgoing interests. There must be a balance between meditation and fellowship. On the one hand, a person may withdraw for solitary communion with God where he can complain about his hurts and express the bitterness of his soul or thank God for his blessings. On the other hand, he must be reminded of the world about him. One who loves God should also love his fellow men. He who gives a cup of cold water in Christ's name does not lose his reward. Service in this world issues from and becomes a form of personal devotion. The mystic and the prophet are blended into one. If the nurse can accept a patient's desire to remain in the protected shelter of sickness and yet remind him of the greater rewards of companionship and a sense of worthiness that comes from a place in society, she has done well.

When patients say they have nothing to live for or are faced with long-term convalescence, the spiritual work is more complicated. Minna Fields has written *Patients Are People* to help others understand the human-relation problems of convalescing patients.[5] For the person who is recovering from illness and says, "I have nothing to live for," there are several avenues of approach. For one thing, the nurse can reflect the patient's feeling and say that she understands how a person might feel that way at times. In response, the patient may then give some explanation, such as, "I'll be going to an empty house" or, "My children are all married." Instead of rebuking the patient or urging him to "buck up," the nurse can ask what the family thinks. This often

---

[5] New York: Columbia University Press, 1953.

reminds the patient that he does have someone to live for. It may also be a reminder that what life requires from us is as important for living as what we require from life.

If the patient has no friends or relatives, the problem is more serious. In such a situation the hospital staff may become a substitute for the patient's family. If the sick one says bitterly, "There is no one who cares for me," the nurse may reply, "You may be thinking of people outside the hospital, but I want you to know that your fight for life has been an inspiration to many of us here. We think of you and pray for you daily." This reminds the patient both that persons whom he can see are concerned about him and that God whom he does not see also cares. A clergyman told a terminally ill patient, who was fully aware of his condition, that the courage with which he was facing a slow death was a source of inspiration to everyone in the church. He looked up in amazement and said, "You mean that people ask about *me?* That they pray for me?" The minister replied, "They not only pray that you will have strength, but they also thank God for the inspiration which you are giving them."

Terminal Illness

It is obvious that the processes of illness which have just been described do not always bring renewed health. The illness may be prolonged. It may be chronic or crippling. The patient may gradually lose ground in a terminal illness or may suddenly die. Under these circumstances the nurse is faced with two problems. First, there is the testing of her own attitude toward life and death. Does she accept death as a part of life, or does it come as an unknown and unwelcomed stranger? Second, death is a humbling experience to professional people who have fought with all their skill to preserve life. It seems that medicine has failed and death has triumphed again. The student nurse may be plagued with questions such as, "Am I responsible for this man's death?" or, "Did I do all that I could to help him?" These are natural questions that arise when we first face the failure of our efforts against illness.

The staff's awareness of this failure often comes during the terminal stage of illness, especially when the doctor has told the staff and some members of the family that the patient will probably not recover. All that he can do has been done. The nurse finds herself in the position of caring for a patient who will probably die while she ministers to him. Furthermore, the patient may suspect that he will die, or he may have been told of his impending death by the physician or by a member of the family.

During his hospitalization, the nurse may observe a psychological "tunneling" process in the patient. This has been described by Dr. Beatrix Cobb of the Medical Psychology Section of the M. D. Anderson Hospital. In the early stages of cancer the patient may be socially alert and interested in world affairs, but as the disease progresses, these interests are "lopped off" one by one. Eventually, one or two members of the family seem to be singled out for emotional support. The nurse and the doctor are held as shields against the fear of pain and death. At last the tunnel seems so narrow that it contains only the battle between the patient and the disease as he awaits relief in death.

Religiously speaking, some patients who are slowly dying seem to go through a stage of resistance against the diagnosis and believe that cancer happens only to "somebody else." When the diagnosis can no longer be avoided, there seems to be a period of bargaining with God in which the patient says, "If you will grant my life, I will do thus and so." When bargaining fails, bitterness may descend upon the soul until there comes a feeling of, "Thy will be done." After this the patient is at peace and seems able to meet death with quiet courage.

Should the Patient Know the Truth?

Facing death with a patient is never easy, but it is more difficult when the patient asks questions about death and has not been told the truth by his physician.

The nurse must hold personal convictions and professional objectivity in balance at such a crucial time. It is difficult to measure the feelings of another person against our own in the face of such an emotional issue as death. The varied thoughts and circumstances of the one who is ill must be patiently considered.

What may be the answer for the nurse may not be the appropriate answer for a patient at this time.

When death is imminent, one of the first objectives is to understand the patient's personal concerns. One summer day a victim of leukemia asked his nurse, "Do you think I will last until fall?" After a moment of complete silence the nurse managed to utter, "What makes you ask this?" Then she quickly changed the subject. The nurse had started out in the right direction, but she was so afraid of what the patient might say that she abruptly moved to another subject. In this case, the patient was more open with his problem than the nurse. He returned to the hospital a few months later and told the nurse several times that there was nothing left for him but to die. The patient's willingness to talk gave courage to the nurse, and they discussed freely the relationship between his condition and his religious beliefs. As a result, the patient was strengthened spiritually even while he weakened physically. On his final admission, he told the nurse that God was his best friend and that he had put his life into God's hands. Several days later he became critically ill and died.

A nurse's interest in the patient's feelings may give him an opportunity to talk about his fear of a disease. Talking often brings relief. A forty-five-year-old woman asked a student nurse, "Do I have cancer?" The nurse replied, "Do you think you have cancer?" The patient said that she was desperately afraid that this might be her condition. She believed that her physician was being evasive about it and that this proved the hopelessness of her case. The nurse suggested that fear might cause her to read more into the doctor's manner than was actually there. She urged the woman to discuss this fear with her doctor. The doctor would certainly want to know what was troubling her because it was making her restless and apprehensive. Although the woman did not talk to her doctor, the nurse wrote later, "The rest of the day she seemed more relaxed, not because I had helped her with my answers, but because someone had taken time to listen to her fears. She told me later that she felt I was her friend in a hospital that had seemed so lonely."

When a nurse's anxiety about death is too great, she cannot

discuss the subject even with a patient who wants to talk about it. In "The Magnificence of Understanding," Nurse Ilse Wolff has described a nurse who had strong feelings of guilt whenever she entered the room of a patient who was in the late stages of bacterial endocarditis. She, a young nurse, was going to live while he, the patient her own age, was about to die. She knew that the patient wished to talk to her, but she would always say something light or give him evasive reassurance. As the patient saw her desperate attempts to escape and felt her anxiety, he took pity on her and kept to himself that which he wished to share with another human being.[6]

Some patients will speak freely about death; others may not. Many patients have to get ready to accept the inevitable. If the nurse is willing to follow the patient's lead at whatever stage he is in his search for truth, then she will find it much easier to steer through the uncharted regions of the soul. On her second admission in two months, one patient was looking dejectedly out the window when her nurse came in.

NURSE: Good afternoon, Mrs. Smith. I am Miss Brown.

PATIENT: Oh, yes.

NURSE: I belive that I had the pleasure of being your nurse when you were here several weeks ago.

PATIENT (*with a very dejected look*): Yes, I have been in and out a number of times.

NURSE: I know this is not easy on you.

PATIENT: Well, it hasn't been too bad. (*looking up with an expression of conviction*) One thing I *do* know,—I'll not put up with pain. It frightens me to think of a painful, slow death.

NURSE: Are you in pain now?

PATIENT: It is not too bad now, but it can only get worse.

NURSE: Oh? I am sorry to hear this. Is this what the doctor has told you?

PATIENT: Yes. (*Turns her head back toward the wall.*)

Two days later the patient asked the same nurse a question.

---

[6] Samuel Standard and Helmuth Nathan, *Should the Patient Know the Truth?* (New York: Springer Publishing Company, 1955), p. 32.

PATIENT: What do they teach you about cancer?

NURSE: The doctors teach us that some cancer is curable and that the patients who cannot be cured can at least be made comfortable. Is that what you wanted to know, Mrs. Smith?

PATIENT: I guess so. Well (*with a sigh*), everyone has to go sometime.

NURSE: Sometime, yes. Do you think this is the time for you?

PATIENT: That is what the doctor told my sister. He said I had cancer.

NURSE: You have not talked with him about this yourself?

PATIENT: Why should I? There is nothing he can do for me.

NURSE: I know how this news must make you feel, Mrs. Smith, but it is better to get it directly. Only the doctor can tell you what he can do. It will strengthen you to talk with him.

PATIENT: I am not afraid—that is, of death.

NURSE: You have faith? (*Patient nods her head.*) I notice that you are from out of town, Mrs. Smith. Would you like for our chaplain to call on you since your pastor cannot visit you often?

PATIENT: Yes, that would be nice.

In this example, the nurse was willing first to follow the patient's feelings of despair. Second, she gave a simple answer to the question about cancer. Very often, the first opportunity that a nurse has to "tell the truth" is when she can provide simple explanations of procedures and treatments. To be most helpful, the nurse must know what information the patient and his family have already been given by the doctor. Some brief conversation between the nurse and the doctor about this is most important. Third, the nurse waited for the patient to unfold her fears. Fourth, she knew the limitations of her own professional role and made the proper referrals for information to the doctor and for pastoral care to the chaplain.

Telling the truth, therefore, is not just a matter of answering point-blank questions. It involves the total attitude toward the patient, willingness to talk about matters of importance to him, and ease and an openness in ministering to his needs. This will be especially true with children, who seem to accept the fact of serious illness without prolonged explanations. Nurse Ruth Baer recalls an experience when a child died suddenly in his sleep. The nurses carefully told the children that he had been transferred to another part of the hospital. Later in the day Nurse Baer heard one of the children tell another, "Johnny died, but don't tell the nurses." [7]

A nurse cannot be her best with a patient when a doctor has lied to a patient about his condition and ordered the nurses to do likewise. In the symposium *Should the Patient Know the Truth?* most of the doctors who opposed "the truth" pointed to cancer as the dread disease about which few patients should be told. But one of the physicians who believed that the patient should know his condition recalled that there was a time when a patient who had tuberculosis was not told because doctors thought it would undermine his confidence in recovery.[8]

The attitudes of the nurse and the physician toward death are another major factor in the question, "Should the patient know the truth?" The patient's feelings have been discussed first because professional persons should not rush in with their own answers upon the assumption that others feel exactly as they do. Having spoken these words of caution, it should be emphasized that the nurses' and doctors' philosophy of death is also of crucial importance.

When the question of death arises, it appears that many professional persons read their own private needs into the patient's problem. Their answers are often different from those which patients would wish. For example, when Professor Russell Dicks asked physicians, "Do you think a person facing death should be told what he is facing if he asks?" 59.8 per cent replied yes. In reply to his second question, "If he does not ask?" 11.9 per cent answered yes.

When patients are asked if they want to know the truth about their conditions, the percentages are quite different. Drs. W. D. Kelly and S. R. Friesen found that 89 of 100 cancer patients and 82 of 100 noncancer patients said that they preferred to know the truth about their condition. Of a group of 740 healthy people getting a routine yearly physical examination, 98.5 per cent said they wanted to be told should they develop cancer. Twenty-

[7] "The Sick Child Knows," *ibid.*, p. 102.

[8] Dr. Isidore Snapper, "Other Times, Other Fears," *ibid.*, p. 87.

four patients in the cancer group were asked if the knowledge that they had cancer had in any way altered their routine or style of living outside of any physical disability. The answer was no in all cases. One year after the study, 41 cancer patients were contacted by mail and were asked if their feelings were still the same. Answers were obtained in 31 cases. Two had died; 29 answered essentially as they did before. The doctors concluded from this research that patients want to be informed of the nature of their illness to a far greater extent than the average physician would anticipate.[9]

Grave spiritual problems are raised when nurses, doctors, chaplains, and ministers enter into a conspiracy with the family of a dying patient to withhold information from him when he is rational. By "conspiracy" is meant a consciously contrived mood of deception. The opposite of this is not a compulsive desire to blurt out a calculated guess about the date of the person's death. An attitude of acceptance and courage is urged: acceptance by the staff that death is a part of life which has been spiritually overcome through Christ, and courage to answer the patient's questions, as well as respond to his moods and help him to talk about death and eternal life. This means that the nurse, the doctor, and the minister must approach the patient with a willingness to accept the fact that earthly life does end. It also means that they will actively encourage the patient to put into words his own feelings. If a terminally ill patient says, "The doctors haven't told me yet what my condition is," the nurse may reply, "What do you think your condition is?" This attitude also implies some specific inquiry about the patient's relationship to God when the patient seems to be unaware of his condition and has never indicated an interest in the state of his soul.

What concern should the nurse have for the eternal salvation of the patient? The burden of this responsibility can be borne by different people. Sometimes the physician may tell the patient that he can do nothing more than make him comfortable and may urge him to talk with his spiritual adviser. Sometimes the

---

[9] "Do Cancer Patients Want to Be Told?" *Surgery*, 27 (1950), 822–26.

patient will ask for his pastor, priest, or rabbi. On occasion he may want the doctor to be his minister. On one occasion a patient grasped his physician's arm and said, "You are a man of faith. What would *you* do?"

On other occasions a member of the family may be the first one to tell the patient that his illness is fatal. Then the patient may talk of death or he may wait to discuss his spiritual concerns with a more trusted member of the family or a friend. The doctor or family member may suggest that the patient's clergyman call. In addition, it will be helpful to the patient if they witness to their own faith.

Whether others have spoken to the patient of death or not, the nurse may be confronted by her patient with questions about the spiritual significance of death. Here is an example:

I [the nurse] had become well acquainted with Mr. J. during his two weeks in the hospital. I had also met his wife and had seen his children in the lobby. As I was asking about his children one day, he said:

PATIENT: Do you think I have as good a chance as anyone to go to heaven?

NURSE: Why, yes, I think everyone has a chance to go to heaven.

PATIENT: Well, that is what I think too. (*pause*)

NURSE: You have been doing some thinking about this?

PATIENT: Who doesn't when they are facing what I have? I think I have been a pretty good man. I never was much for church, though. My wife likes to go and used to want me to go, too. I guess I will never get to go again.

NURSE: Do you believe that you can go to heaven even if you are not in the church?

PATIENT: Yes, but now I wish I had gone with my wife. She is a good woman. Did she say what time she was coming by today?

The nurse had courage to give a straight-forward answer to the question about heaven. She then asked the patient about his thinking. But thereafter she moved in too fast with the question about salvation and the church. Since Mr. J. had mentioned his wife's interest in the church, the nurse might have asked the name and the denomination of the church which his wife attended. She could have asked if Mr. J. preferred this church or if he had some preference of his own. In this way she could have encouraged him to express his own interest in religion. It would then have been easy for her to ask him if he would like for the chaplain or the minister of the church of his preference to call on him. The nurse could also have assured Mr. J. of her continued interest in his spiritual welfare since she considered it very important for him and for every other patient. This would have given Mr. J. an opportunity to continue to discuss religion with her at the same time that other spiritual counsel was being sought. Mr. J. raised a question of eternal significance, and the nurse responded as best she could. To turn aside the question or to show a lack of interest would have demonstrated a lack of feeling for the patient's concern.

It is hoped that in most hospitals the nurse will have the cooperation of the chaplain, the pastor, and the doctor so that it will not be necessary for her to confront the issue of eternal salvation alone with the patient. In hospitals with a department of religion the chaplain is usually notified of all critical cases. It is his responsibility to inquire into the spiritual welfare of patients at such a time. If the patient or members of his family express anxiety to the nurse concerning death, she may ask if their pastor has been called. If they have no pastor, she may assist them in finding one if the hospital has no chaplain.

Thus far in this chapter the discussion has dealt with patients whose spiritual condition is in doubt. There are also those who profess faith in Jesus Christ or belong to a Jewish synagogue. This raises a second theological concern for a truthful approach to a patient. In the Judaic-Christian tradition death has always been looked upon as a spiritual experience. The way in which a Christian dies may be a great lesson for his family and a source of courage and strength to his friends and companions. If he is not told or if there is no indication that he knows, the issue is always in doubt and people will say, "Well, he died bravely, but then I don't think he ever knew."

It is especially important for a Christian to know his condition if he becomes hostile toward his family, acts impatient with the doctors and nurses, and drifts without an inner purpose. A fifty-year-old man was told by his physician that an exploratory operation revealed a malignancy which could not be removed. The doctor saw the chaplain several minutes later, told him what he had found, and urged him to visit the patient. Shortly after the chaplain entered the room the patient said, "What do I have to live for? All of the things that I have worked for so hard will now fall apart." The chaplain replied, "Well, I can understand how you would feel this way after the initial shock of such news. Do you want to tell me what you have in mind?" In the edifying conversations which followed, this father found a great purpose in dying well.

The serenity of this Protestant patient was akin to that of a Catholic patient who has received extreme unction. For in Catholic moral theology the doctor is obligated in charity and justice to warn the patient in danger of death. The Catholic doctor is morally bound to see that a non-Catholic who is dying shall have opportunity to prepare his soul for eternity. Sister Bernadette Armiger states, "Sparing the patient knowledge of the truth savors of misguided sentimentality and false humanitarianism." [10]

The nurse must not disregard the condition of her patient just because eternity is not important to her own theology. It may be very important to the patient and to his family. This should be as carefully considered for a Protestant as for a Roman Catholic. It is also advisable to be courageous rather than passive when eternal issues are at stake. When a patient talks about death, the nurse can help lead him toward a greater source of strength which comes through personal surrender to God. When a patient does not raise any questions, she can cultivate an attitude which would encourage such conversation and notify the chaplain of the patient's spiritual condition. The nurse in charge of the unit may take responsibility for routine notification of the critically ill to the chaplain's office.

---

[10] "Ethics in Nursing Responsibility," Standard, *op. cit.*, p. 128.

8. Ministry to the Bereaved

IN OLD TESTAMENT TIMES it was believed that a person was already near Sheol [1] when any calamity befell him. In the grave or the pit, called Hades or Sheol, life was thought to continue in a weaker or more subdued state. It was the abode of misfortune, pain, and trouble.[2]

By the time of Christ such Jewish writings as the book of Enoch, which is included in the Apocrypha, presented strong convictions concerning life after death in either heaven or hell. The grave no longer was a place of hazy existence but was seen as a two-story domain in which the good people dwelt in a paradise and the evil ones in a place of fire, Gehenna. Jesus referred to this division of the grave in his story of the rich man and Lazarus.[3]

In New Testament teachings the shadowy existence and terror of death were overcome through the victory of Christ's death and resurrection. Physical death was not the end point of existence. The real crisis of life came when a person accepted Christ as Lord and Saviour. It was at this time that he took present possession of eternal life.[4] Surrender to God in this life through Christ is a guarantee of eternal life now and forever.

Since the emphasis of the New Testament was upon spiritual life, there was no speculation about the exact physical char-

---

[1] Job 33:22; 28:30; Psalms 8; 116; Jonah 2:1–6.
[2] Hos. 13:4; Psalm 116:3. [3] Luke 16:19–31.
[4] Gal. 2:20; 2 Cor. 5:6–9; Phil. 1:21.

acteristics of persons after death. Paul wrote: "It is sown a physical body. It is raised a spiritual body." [5] Personal faith in Christ's triumph over death took the place of philosophical Greek and other pagan speculation. Therefore, there is little that the Christian can say in response to questions about the recognition of people in heaven or the exact state of the resurrected body. We do know that heaven is where God dwells [6] and that hell is to be a place of destruction, condemnation, and punishment.[7] It is assumed that there will be some recognizable characteristics in our resurrection bodies,[8] but our earthly ties will be glorified. In the resurrection we do not marry or are given in marriage but are like the angels in heaven.[9] The great hope of the Christian is that in the world to come he will be like Christ.[10]

Today there is no unanimity of opinion among religious leaders about life after death. Some clergymen, patients, and nurses will believe that persons who do not accept Jesus Christ as Lord and Saviour must stand before God in the last judgment. Those who have rejected Christ and chosen other gods will be condemned to eternity apart from God, because God respects the choices of men. Others do not believe that God would ever cast one of his creatures away for eternity. For "an age" they may be separated from him, but not "forever." God's love will eventually bring them all back to his fellowship. A third view is that judgment is a relative thing. We do not really know how God will determine our future, so we should suspend judgment ourselves. The statements in the Bible concerning judgment are looked upon as evidence that was sufficient for the first century but which may be superseded by a more "complete" revelation sometime in the future. A fourth view is that all people live after death in a shadowy existence where there is no distinction between good and evil. A few persons believe that all existence ends with death. Finally, there are some people who will not think about death at all.

---

[5] 1 Cor. 15:44.
[6] Matt. 6:9.
[7] Mark 9:43–47; Matt. 18:8; 13:42, 50.
[8] Luke 24.
[9] Matt. 23:30.
[10] 1 John 3:2–3.

The Circumstances Surrounding Death

Whatever our theological belief, death comes as a tremendous experience. To the relative it is the parting with someone who has been dearly beloved, cordially hated, or indifferently accepted. To the nurse it is a difficult task of losing a fight for one who has needed constant care and noble courage. To the patient it is the step into the very presence of God.

The circumstances which surround death will influence a nurse's and the family's reaction to it. Death may come either as an intruder or as a welcomed visitor. It is an intruder when it comes in the form of a sudden heart attack or an accident. Death may appear as an intruder in the violence of suicide, murder, or electrocution; in the mystery of a child who never wakes up or a patient whose heart stops during surgery; or in the shame of a sister's whisper, "My sister's husband died in a car wreck with another woman." On the other hand, death may come as a welcomed visitor when suffering has been prolonged and much pain has been experienced by both the patient and the family.

The manner of death is one important factor in understanding a family's grief. It will also have an effect upon the staff of the hospital. When death is expected, the hospital personnel can prepare themselves, the patient, and the family for it. But when a young, healthy mother dies during childbirth or a teen-age boy dies during an operation in which no complications were expected, it is more difficult for the staff to accept and interpret such tragedy to the family.

A second circumstantial factor is the attitude of the family toward the patient and the nurse during a terminal illness. If the relatives have been very appreciative of the nurse's ministry, she can enter into the family grief with confidence and acceptance. But if members of the family have let it be known that they think the nurses are not doing what they ought to do, it is difficult for nurses to overcome hostile reactions and be sympathetic with the family.

If the illness has brought the family together in love and courage, the staff and other patients are inspired. If a dying father knows about his condition and talks with his wife about heaven, the care of the children, and her future financial condition, the nurse may feel privileged to be a part of this great drama of religious faith and family devotion.

But it can be otherwise. A young man who had married against his parents' wishes was hospitalized in the terminal stages of leukemia. His parents, who had ignored him completely from the day of his engagement, rushed to his side. They smothered him with attention. They jealously watched the nurses and doctors who entered "their" room. The young man's wife was expecting a child within two months. The parents did not offer to bring her to the hospital on any occasion. When she was able to come on the bus, they sat in icy silence while she talked with her husband. As soon as possible, they would send her on some errand or ask her to go home since, they said, "the boy needs to rest." The parents insisted on paying all of the bills, and the doctor told them that the boy was dying. He did not bother to speak to the young wife. The parents kept the information from her for several weeks. Finally, three days before their son died, they told his wife that he would not live very long. They offered her no emotional or financial support but turned immediately to a discussion of the type of funeral they would have.

As anyone might know, the nurses identified themselves with the young wife and could hardly maintain a civil attitude toward the possessive parents. For weeks after the young man was buried, many of the nurses could not think of the incident without rage at the selfishness and cruelty of the parents.

A third factor in the nurse's and the family's reaction to death will be the attitude and work of the physician. If the doctor has told the patient the truth and has dealt gently with the family, the nurse gains courage from his example and identifies herself with his character. No matter how difficult the management of the patient may become, the nurse is secure in the knowledge that a competent doctor has done all he can for the patient and has left judicious orders for the nurse to follow.

When a doctor is cold to the family and negligent of the patient, nurses are uneasy about their ministry to the patient and hostile toward the doctor. A student nurse observed that the sickness of a four-year-old girl seemed to be getting worse and called the family pediatrician. About six hours later he came, but only after another doctor had examined the child and called him again. He immediately performed a procedure that seemed to be hasty and ill advised in the eyes of the student nurses and supervisors. The child died during this procedure. The pediatrician then went to the parents and told them of the child's death. The nurses who heard this conversation thought he was careless and matter of fact in his presentation. As the student nurses talked this over with their nursing instructor and the chaplain, they analyzed the causes of their resentment against the doctor as stemming from his neglect of the patient, hasty action, and callousness to the family. The chaplain pointed out that they also were incensed because this was a child. One of the nurses replied that if it had been an older person, "who might have died anyway," she might not have felt so badly.

How does a nurse get over such feelings? In this case the student nurses were encouraged to talk out their feelings with instructors and other experienced nurses. They also had an opportunity to ventilate their feelings with the chaplain. Thus they were able to work out their aggressions and frustrations in a secure atmosphere and benefit from the judgment and analysis of the problem by experienced professional people.

From discussions such as these the students could develop a more mature perspective in several ways. A student nurse rarely calls the attending physician unless she is instructed to do so by the supervisor. Usually a student reports her observations to a graduate nurse or supervisor. The supervisor checks the student's observations and calls the intern or resident physician if she thinks it advisable. The resident physician checks the patient and then, if he cannot cope with the situation, calls the attending physician. It is not necessary for the student to take that responsibility.

Emergency procedures often offer the only hope of recovery. A member of the staff may show poor judgment, but criticism should be tempered by knowledge of what might have occurred if he had not acted quickly. Neglect may be apparent or real. If the physician is taking care of other seriously ill patients, probably in another hospital, his delay will not be intentional. In such circumstances another physician should be called by the supervisor. A doctor who is negligent, exercises poor judgment, and is callous toward the family of his patients will probably not stay in one community very long.

A fourth factor which conditions the nurse's reaction to death will be her own work with the patient. If a student feels that she has done all a nurse should, she is reassured. But on other occasions the nurse may be tormented with doubts about herself after a patient dies. A sixty-five-year-old man with a severe heart condition began to slip down into his bed until he was precariously near the edge. The nurse pulled him back up on the bed as gently as she could. Within an hour the patient was dead. The student wondered if her action had been responsible for his death. Fortunately, she discussed this with her nursing instructor as well as the head nurse. The head nurse suggested that she get the help of other students or an orderly if the moving of a patient should ever be difficult, but neither she nor the instructor felt that this motion endangered the patient's life. In fact, it was a necessary procedure if the patient were not to fall from the bed.

When a nurse does feel guilty or concerned about her work with a patient who is terminally ill, she may reassure herself by talking it over with her friends and experienced members of the staff. She, or they, may bring out the fact that her work was a necessary part of nursing. No one can make a patient live forever, no matter how diligent the professional care may be. The death of a patient may be the first personal defeat which a nurse experiences. It will not be her last, and she will be helped by the philosophy which instructors, chaplains, and doctors have acquired through their years of similar experience.

When a patient dies, a nurse may find that she is making herself excessively busy with many routines which are not required of her so that she will not have time to be with the one who is dying. She should look upon this action as a sign of her own anxiety. There are numerous details which are a part of a nurse's work at the time of death. These are important ways of handling the natural anxiety connected with grief. But this is different from an over-efficient concern for minute details which will distract the nurse from any care of the family or recognition of the psychological impact of death.

If the nurse will consider the circumstances that surround death, she may use them to help the family obtain perspective. If a patient and family have known for months that he would not recover, they probably have grieved over a long period of time. The death may come as somewhat of a relief, and the student nurse can say, "You have grieved for him so long that now his death comes as a release from suffering." On the other hand, when a year-old baby is brought into the emergency room and dies shortly after arrival, the nurse should realize that this is a great shock. The parents may be numb or overwhelmed with grief.

After the pediatrician had told a young couple that their three-day-old baby had died, the wife tried to hold back her tears while the husband sat numbly in a chair. The nursing supervisor took the young man to her office with the words, "You need a place where you can be alone for a few minutes and give in to your own feelings." After a brief interval, she went back to her office and said, "You have had a good cry by yourself, but you and your wife need to express your grief together. Do not be afraid to let her know how you feel, for she needs to feel that you lean on her at the same time she leans upon you."

After the husband first left his wife, the student nurse who stayed said to her, "I know what a great shock this is to you. You may feel numb all over. But don't hold back the tears." After the mother had cried for a while, the husband returned, and the two of them embraced each other for a few minutes. When the husband began to control himself, the student nurse said that the hospital chaplain had been called and would be with them in a few minutes. She asked if there were any friends or relatives or a pastor whom she might call for them. About this time the chaplain came in. The student nurse introduced him to the grieving parents and excused herself. She went to the nursing station and told the charge nurse that the chaplain was now with the family.

In both these illustrations the nurses were aware of the process of grief as well as its circumstances. Only a part of this process is usually observed in a hospital setting, but it is well for the nurse to know all that it involves.

The Process of Grief

Grief is a process. It often begins with a numbing effect in which the mourner says, "I'm frozen up inside," "It seems so dark," or "I just can't feel." The nurse may explain that this is one of the ways that nature helps a person to withstand the first shock of grief. The "little things" which the nurse does in the first shock of bereavement are very meaningful. She may explain that she has called the chaplain, offer to call some member of the family, offer a chair to the relative who is standing, or suggest that the family sit in the waiting room or chapel where they can grieve quietly. Sometimes she can put her arm about a child and explain to him that it will help mother to cry now that daddy is dead. The nurse may take the child out of the room and sit down with him in some quiet place where the child can be encouraged to ask any questions or show any feelings that need to be experienced.

Hysteria sometimes is seen among relatives immediately after death of a loved one. Some relatives think that they are expected to scream and tear their hair. Under those conditions the nurse, the doctor, or the chaplain may need to remind them kindly that there are other patients in the hospital who are being disturbed. This is like setting limits on childish behavior by saying, "You may do things like that in your house, but we don't do things like that here."

Hysteria may also be seen in people who feel very guilty. They say to themselves, and sometimes to others, "He must not die, for I must make up for all the things that I have done to him." This guilt cannot be relieved at once. The individual often must be led from the hospital. Sedatives, psychiatric treatment, and pastoral counseling are often necessary follow-ups.

Nurses sometimes call a doctor for a tranquilizer to give to a grieving relative who is not hysterical. This should not be a routine procedure, since medication like this may postpone the reality of death which the bereaved must face. Consultation with the chaplain or pastor about the emotional state of relatives will be helpful. The pastor can often evaluate the grieving one's degree of emotional control because he has known the person for some time. Both pastor and chaplain will have had enough experience with grief to give some counsel to the nurse. Of course, the final decision concerning medication will come from the doctor.

The reality of death must be faced. Relatives should not be told that a patient has "expired." Mourners need to hear the words dead, death, funeral, cemetery, and grave. All of these phrases do not come from the nurse, but she need not avoid any of them. Without the sympathetic realistic assistance of the staff, mourners may allow grief to slide into fantasy. The unhealthy end of such unreality is an idealization of "the departed one."

When the finality of death has been conveyed by the staff to relatives, it is easier for them to resolve the struggle between fantasy and reality. This is the second stage of grief. It usually appears after the funeral, as the mourner feels, "I just can't believe that he is really gone."

A flood of grief often comes as the third stage in bereavement. There is deep anguish and despair as the person finally realizes that the loved one is dead. There is very little reassurance that can easily be given at such a time.

A fourth step in the process of grief is the selective memory and stabbing pain that comes in the weeks or months that follow death. This is a time for a pastor to listen carefully to the mourner and the time for friends, relatives, and the church to listen, understand, and support.

A fifth stage in grief may be seen in patients who have lost a loved one a few weeks or a month before entering the hospital for surgical or medical care. Many of these patients have developed daytime reveries in which memories of the deceased fill their minds. At night they may have dreams of the loved one who is gone. Sometimes these day and night fantasies are sexual or hostile in nature. In such instances religious doubts and persecutory feelings may appear. A patient may say, "God has left me," "I have committed the unpardonable sin," or "I cannot pray."

This is a crucial period, since the mourner may regress to an earlier stage of development and begin to depend upon others for decisions that he should make. Sometimes the mourner becomes fixed at this stage of grief and never moves on to the development of new interests. This stage is known as "a delayed grief reaction." The person develops definite depressive or other symptoms of mourning. A fifty-year-old woman came into the hospital with a complaint of "a feeling of fish hooks in my throat." Her husband had died suddenly a year before she entered the hospital. A well-intentioned cousin told her that she should bear up and not express any grief. After a year of repression, tears would not come although she wished to cry.

Following six interviews with the chaplain, in which they discussed the relief that comes from mourning, she began to cry. The chaplain told her to "cry it out"; he would leave her alone for a little while. He told the nurses what the patient was experiencing. About half an hour later, when a student nurse went into the room, she found that the patient had gone to sleep for the first time during the day without sedatives. After three more days of medical attention and pastoral counseling, the woman went home feeling that her burden was lifted.

The final stage in the normal process of grief is the development of new interests and the transference of love to new objects. The interests of the mourner are turned to problems of work, children, or perhaps remarriage.

Theologically, the great conflict of bereavement is between idolatry and the way of the cross. In idolatry, the deceased is idealized and the dead is kept emotionally alive. In the way of the cross, the mourner receives courage from God to relive the painful memories of death, accept the physical reality of the grave, and pour out his feelings of despair and rebellion before men and his Maker. The doctrine of the resurrection gives him strength to rebuild his own life. First Corinthians 15 and 2 Corinthians 5 assert that the strength of Christ's resurrection is in the heart of the Christian even in the face of weakness and death.

Education for Death

Many of the problems which were discussed under the section on depression are also examples of the grief experience. An amputee may grieve for the limb that has been removed. The divorcee may grieve over her broken marriage and her loneliness. A broken courtship may often be a bereavement situation. Persons who speak of the unpardonable sin may be laboring under heavy grief or the hurt of a loveless life.

Children are often prepared for grief through the loss of pets or the death of grandparents, uncles, or aunts. Homesickness, the removal of playmates to a different city, or a major conflict with someone who was close to them may also precipitate grief. There are two articles which will help nurses to explain death to children. One, by Pauline Best, is "An Experience in Interpreting Death to Children." [11] In it she tells how a Sunday school teacher led her class of five-year-olds to talk about one of the group who had recently died. The children described all of the good and the bad things about their former classmate and seemed to be much less anxious about his loss after they had discussed it freely with an adult. The second is one by Helen H. Sherrill, "Interpreting Death to Children." It is available in pamphlet form from the Department of Publication, National Council of Churches, 297 Fourth Avenue, New York 10, New York.

For Further Reading:

Children and parents: A pamphlet "On the Death of a Child" (Forward Movement Publications, 412 Sycamore Street, Cincinnati 2, Ohio) is an actual letter written by an Episcopal clergyman to his daughter, whose little son had died with cruel suddenness. Mary Boazman has described "The Adaptation of

[11] *Journal of Pastoral Care*, II (Spring, 1948), 29–34.

Mothers to the Sudden Loss of Their Children Through Leukemia," *Cancer*, VIII (Jan., 1955), 1–19.

Autopsies: Since relatives are often troubled about autopsies, the *Reader's Digest* for April, 1956, printed an article by Albert Maisel, "The Truth About Autopsies." Reprints are available at nominal cost from the *Reader's Digest.*

Process of grief: Extensive discussion about bereavement in the family may be found in Thomas D. Elliott's "The Bereaved Family" [12] and Howard Becker, "The Sorrow of Bereavement." [13] The original research upon which much of our descriptions of bereavement depends is Dr. Erick Lindenman's study of the relatives and victims of the Coconut Grove fire in 1944.[14]

Normal and abnormal mourning: The theological issues in mourning, the complications of delayed grief reactions, and abnormal grief reactions are described by Paul Irion, *The Funeral and the Mourners;* [15] Wayne Oates, *Anxiety in Christian Experience;* [16] and Edgar Jackson, *Understanding Grief.*[17]

Thoughts of the dying: The thought processes of a dying man are described fictionally by Leo Tolstoy in "The Death of Ivan Ilyich." [18] A layman's view of the dying patient and those who attend him may be found in George Orwell's "How the Poor Die." [19] An excellent pamphlet which may be given to the bereaved is *When You Lose a Loved One* [20] by Ernest Osborne. James Agee's *Death in the Family* [21] is a beautiful portrayal of a whole family's reaction to the father's accidental death.

[12] *The Annals of the American Academy of Political and Social Science,* 160 (November, 1955), 184–90.

[13] *Journal of Abnormal and Social Psychology,* 27 (July–Sept., 1932), 391–410.

[14] "Symptomatology and Management of Acute Grief," *American Journal of Psychiatry,* CI (Sept., 1944), 141–49.

[15] New York: Abingdon Press, 1954.

[16] Philadelphia: Westminster Press, 1955.

[17] New York: Abingdon Press, 1957.

[18] *Best Russian Short Stories* (New York: Modern Library, n. d.).

[19] *Shooting an Elephant and Other Essays* (London: Secker & Warburg, 1950).

[20] Public Affairs Pamphlet No. 269.

[21] New York: McDowell-Obolensky, 1957.

9. Resources for the Nurse's Spiritual Ministry

In the preceding chapters many suggestions regarding the nurse's religious ministry to patients have been made. Many of these came from a group of nurses who discussed the Bible in relation to the patient's personal needs. In the first two chapters principles of biblical interpretation and the relationship of theology to human problems were considered. In chapters three through eight specific spiritual crises of illness such as death, bereavement, guilt, despair, loneliness, and anxiety were discussed.

Once a nurse has clarified her thinking about the needs of the patient, she will be ready for some suggestions about specific conversations on religion and the use of the Bible and prayer. This area will be the topic for this chapter. Since the nurse's religious ministry will be influenced by her hospital, it is necessary first to look at the various factors in the hospital which condition her religious ministry. Second, some general principles of religious conversation will be considered. Finally, the use of specific religious resources such as the Bible and prayer will be discussed.

The Hospital and Religion

Hospitals, like people, take on character and personality. Its spoken and unspoken policies will have great influence upon those who work therein. There are a variety of factors related to the hospital which may have a definite bearing upon a nurse's religious ministry.

One of the most obvious influences is seen in the differences between a large metropolitan university hospital and a small hospital in a county-seat town. In the former, nurses will probably have had no previous contact with the patients. Patients will come from cultural and religious backgrounds which may or may not be familiar to the nurse. This does not mean that a large university hospital is necessarily a place of impersonal relationships. But it does mean that as a rule the nurses have not had intimate contact with the patient, his family, or his neighbors. As a result, religious conversations must be based more specifically on the expressed needs of the patients. This is why a discussion on religious conversation follows chapters on the spiritual crises of illness. The nurse needs to be acquainted with the inner problems of a sick person if she is to make a contribution to the patient's religious life when the opportunity arises.

In the small hospital of a county-seat town, in contrast, the nurse may be well acquainted with the patient's family. Furthermore, the nurse, the patient, and the family may have all grown up in the same culture and share the same social and religious beliefs. The importance of this contrast is obvious for religious conversation. In a small town the nurse probably knows the religious affiliation and the zeal of her patient. If not, a brief "get-acquainted" period usually includes questions about denomination, church, and pastor. The patient and the nurse will probably have a speaking acquaintance on all three of these subjects. Religious conversation comes more naturally, if not inevitably.

The religious affiliation of the hospital will also be important. In church-related hospitals two factors encourage religious conversation. One is the obvious effort of some schools of nursing to obtain students from the churches of the denomination with which the hospital is affiliated. Many students who enter a school of nursing from such churches have a specific desire to profess their faith through a nursing career.

Second, patients who enter a church-related hospital often expect a religious atmosphere. This may come in part from a chaplain, but it might equally be expected from a nurse or any other member of the hospital staff. Patients would not expect as specific an emphasis upon religious service in a county-owned hospital or a small hospital operated by a group of doctors. This is not to imply that either of the latter institutions are irreligious. It simply means that in them the nurse must be more sensitive to the patient's spiritual needs because it is not expected of a nurse to talk about religion.

A third religious influence is the number of professional people who have contact with the patient. The staff of one hospital may be composed of a large number of physicians in private practice, graduate nurses, and students. Except for a daily visit by the physician, a patient may have no one to converse with except a nurse or an occasional visitor. If the patient has any personal problems, she will be more inclined to speak them to the nurse because there is no one else with whom she can talk freely.

In another hospital the situation will be quite different. The patient or his family may be interviewed by a social worker. The chief resident, an intern, and two or three medical students may have contact with the patient. A clinical psychologist or a psychiatrist may visit the patient. Licensed vocational nurses, nurses' aides, and auxiliary personnel from the library and volunteer services may also be in and out of the patient's room. Under these circumstances nursing students, like medical students, may wonder what they are to do.

Not only are there many people talking with the patient, but some individuals are so insecure in their professional position that they jealously guard "their field." Therefore, if the patient should begin to tell a nurse about her home life, the nurse may think uneasily that the social worker will be displeased. If another patient wishes to discuss the quirks of his personality, the nurse may divert him because she knows that the psychiatric resident is already working with this patient. If the patient wishes to talk about religion, the nurse may wonder what the chaplain or one of his assistants has been saying to this patient.

Therefore, in an institution where many professional people

see one patient, the nurse tends to feel less responsibility and have less opportunity for conversation of a personal and religious nature with the patient.

The question of supervision is also important. When there is "tight" or "strict" control of student and graduate nurses, there may be little personal interplay between patient and nurse. The nurse is afraid to "step out of line." Not only does she feel that this is forbidden by her supervisor, but she knows little about the patient. On the other hand, when student and graduate nurses are taught to take their share of the responsibility for the patient's human needs and receive adequate information in ward conferences on the background and the present status of the patient, the opportunity for religious ministries are manifold. But when nurses are not encouraged to become self-directing, they often end up with the feeling of one student, who said, "I just stood around feeling foolish."

A fifth factor of religion in a hospital will be the attitude of the administration and the medical staff toward student and graduate nurses. In an "old order institution," all nurses must stand when a doctor comes into the room, step aside when he walks into an elevator, and follow his directions without thought of offering a suggestion. Under these conditions the nursing student develops little reliance upon her own abilities as a professional person. She will probably shy away from any but the most superficial religious reassurances and quickly seek some "safe" ground upon which she will not be criticized by her teachers.

Under the "new order," nurses tend to be more self-reliant because their professional status is recognized as next in importance to that of the physician. In a staff conference, for example, the resident physician may present his report and the head nurse will present hers. A supervising nurse in the operating room may be told by a student that a surgeon has "broken the scrub." The supervisor has authority to stop the operation until the surgical field is again sterile. Under this order, a student or graduate can work with new confidence. If a doctor is not pleased with the routine of a nurse, he cannot immediately "blast her down" with his own authority. He must make his report to the nursing supervisor or the administrator.

With these procedures enforced, a student nurse may move with more assurance in the performance of her religious opportunities. If a patient asks her to pray for him before he goes into surgery, she may pray with him and then discuss her action with her instructor or head nurse. She need not fear that any one of a half-dozen superiors will criticize her consecutively for "stepping out of her place." As a matter of fact, under the new system she will probably know more about her place than she would under the old. She is receiving careful supervision from one or more persons who are specifically delegated with the responsibility of teaching her.

A final factor which influences the nurses' spiritual ministry is the department of religion. If there is no chaplain in the hospital and the nurse sees that many patients are not visited by a minister, she may take more religious initiative toward the patients than she would if ministers and chaplains were active on her floor. The number of chaplains will also make a difference. If there is only one chaplain for a five-hundred-bed hospital, the nurse may assume that he is giving little more than superficial reassurance to a large number of patients. Any conversation of depth will still be left to the nurses and to other personnel. The training of the chaplain is another variable. The American Protestant Hospital Association requires six months of clinical training before it will accredit a man as a professional chaplain. A well-trained chaplain will work closely with the nurses so that they can tell him which patients are in special need of his ministry. He will probably teach some classes for the nurses and may even use this textbook. The chaplain's work will be presented more fully in the next chapter.

These varied circumstances indicate the varied influences of the hospital upon religious ministries by the nurse in a hospital. Under none of these conditions would religion be unimportant. The factors which have been enumerated will condition the nurse's religious ministry, but they do not determine whether she will have such a ministry or not.

Listening for Religious Needs

A number of conversations about religion and the spiritual needs of patients have already been given in this book. Some of them, quoted directly from nurses' interviews, indicate that nurses seem to feel forced to give direct answers. They act as though they are expected to solve the patients' problems. Actually, many patients are looking for someone who will listen. They do not want stereotyped answers; they want a sympathetic, understanding ear.

One of the first principles is to listen to what the patient actually says. On some occasions listeners are so preoccupied that they cannot repeat a single word that a person has just said. But a nurse is a trained observer. If she notes with care the actual phrases of a patient, she may have a key by which many of the patient's fears and anxieties may be unlocked. Only to repeat back a phrase may be the encouraging word which will help the patient express himself. As a student nurse was turning away from one patient in a four-bed ward, another patient said to her:

PATIENT: May I talk with you a few minutes?

NURSE: Of course you may.

PATIENT: You know, I have always had a hard time talking to anyone. Most people seem not to have time to listen.

NURSE: I'll take time to listen.

PATIENT: Well, I feel so bad about the way I talk to you nurses when I don't get my hypo on time or my light is not answered immediately. I find myself saying bad things, and then I want to apologize. It takes time for me to get the courage, and by that time you have gone on your way. I tried praying about it, but so far I just haven't made any headway.

NURSE: I guess you just needed to tell one of us about it, didn't you?

PATIENT: Yes, I did, but I felt so ashamed of myself.

NURSE: It takes courage for a man to apologize. (*Patient's eyes begin to water.*) I think that you will feel better, and we will be able to work with you better because of this. (*Patient nods his head.*) You have been under a great strain these past few days. We all recognize how hard it is to be patient when you are in pain and want immediate help.

The patient had worried about this for days, and his condition did not improve. When a nurse stopped for a minute, answered his question, and then noticed the phrase "time to listen," he was encouraged to speak. At the close of this partially reported conversation, the nurse reminded the patient that he had spoken of prayer. She asked him if he would like to talk with his minister or with one of the chaplains. The patient said that he felt much better now, but that if the chaplain wanted to drop by, he would have no objection. The patient may feel a little guilty about his behavior with the nurses, so it would be especially important for the nurse to tell the chaplain what has happened so that he may dispel the patient's fears of a harsh religious lecture.

A second principle of listening is to catch the emotional tone of the patient's phrases. Words may convey deeper meanings to which the nurse must be sensitive. If a nurse is never willing to recognize the presence of despair or evil in a person's life, she will not hear the deeper stirrings of the soul. When the nurse thinks that she is to always "cheer up the patients," she will run away from many serious conversations. A young medical patient who had been in the hospital for several weeks told his nurse:

PATIENT: It seems that trouble is arising for me. (*sigh*)

NURSE: Is there something I can do to help?

PATIENT: My family seems to be getting tired of my being sick and in the hospital. Father is trying to keep up my spirits, but I realize it is hard on him, too.

NURSE: Oh, I am sure you are just imagining things.

PATIENT: Well, my brother was here yesterday, and he seemed to be irritated with me. We have always been so close before. It just worried me to death.

NURSE: Now I am sure that your brother meant nothing by the way he acted. He probably is concerned with your getting well, and he probably wouldn't remember the incident. When we are tired and discouraged, we often look for little things and then interpret them in odd ways.

PATIENT: I hope you are right. I wonder what's good on television this morning?

Instead of accepting the man's deeper feelings, the nurse rejected them. She told the patient that he was imagining things and misinterpreting his own family. No wonder he changed the subject to television!

A third conversational principle in listening is to respond in ways that will help the patient to see his problem more clearly and find alternatives from which he can choose the best solution. The nurse should know more about the hospital, sickness, and personal problems than most of her patients. It is her responsibility to help the patient toward a better perspective of himself and his illness. This is possible if, on the basis of her technical knowledge and human understanding, the nurse outlines for the patient some of the common problems of his illness and suggests various ways in which such problems may be resolved. It is not her business to tell him *the* answer, but she can help him find the answer that will be most satisfying for him.

The wife of a patient spoke to one of his nurses about her desperate need to talk with someone. After the woman spoke of her great fear that her husband's operation might reveal a malignancy, the nurse said:

NURSE: Mrs. R., many people have this kind of fear. I wonder if you have had an opportunity to talk with Mr. R.'s doctor about this?

MRS. R.: Oh, yes, and I have the utmost confidence in him. It's not that, it's just my fear of what might happen. I guess I just don't have faith.

NURSE: You mean faith in the doctor or faith in God? (*Mrs. R. suddenly looked relieved. It seemed as though it made such a difference for someone to mention faith in God.*)

MRS. R.: Yes, it's that faith in God that I need. You know my husband's partner told us that he was praying for us. That has meant so much to us. I guess it's just that we have so much to live for. (*Mrs. R. picked out pictures of her children to show the nurse.*)

NURSE: They are lovely. They give you so much to live for.

MRS. R.: Oh, yes, yes. And if anything happened to him . . .

NURSE: Yes, you need faith and a God who will protect *all* of you at a time like this.

Note that the specific mention of God came as a question from the nurse. She was responding to Mrs. R.'s statement about faith. Also, when Mrs. R. mentioned her children, the nurse pointed to the positive aspects of life and yet did not neglect the anxiety. She related the doctrine of the Holy Spirit to the present situation of this family.

The nurse also told Mrs. R. that she would be praying for her and asked if their minister had been notified of Mr. R.'s coming to the hospital. Mrs. R. had never thought of this and went to the telephone to call.

In the above example, the nurse suggested some religious resources. On other occasions the patient may already have these at hand. This leads to a fourth principle, which is that the nurse should seek to look for and encourage whatever religious experience and faith the patient already possesses. Instead of assuming that religion is something which the nurse or the chaplain must bring to the patient, the nurse may often find that the Spirit of God has already been in the room before the nurse or the chaplain arrives.

If there is any religious foundation already within the patient, the nurse should help the patient use it. A mother had great difficulty giving birth to her second child. On the day after delivery the husband was sitting in the room when a student nurse came in to see if his wife was sleeping. She was. When the nurse commented that the wife seemed to be resting well, the husband said:

HUSBAND: Well, I am glad to know that. It has been rough on both of us. We certainly are glad that this baby is healthy and normal.

NURSE: Why, yes. (*I wondered why he put so much emphasis on "normal."*)

HUSBAND: Well, you see, our first baby was not this way. She was a Mongoloid. It was pretty hard to see all of it. It made me so anxious about this baby. My wife, too. (*pause*) I don't know what I would have done if it had not been for the church.

NURSE: It has been a source of strength?

HUSBAND: It certainly has.

NURSE: In what way?

HUSBAND: The minister—and what the church has meant. I don't think that many of the congregation know of our first child. We've told almost no one. But our minister has been so helpful, and my faith in God has helped me, too.

NURSE: You feel that God has helped you?

HUSBAND: Well, my faith has kept me from being bitter—now. I was at first, but our preacher helped me to see that the way our first child was born was an act of nature. We were not being punished for anything that we've done. The doctor thought that perhaps there wasn't enough oxygen for the embryo.

NURSE: How does your wife feel about this?

HUSBAND: We haven't talked much about it, but she agreed when we were talking with the minister that there was no fault on her part and that God was not trying to hurt our baby because of something that we had done. We just don't think that God works that way.

NURSE: And this type of faith has helped you in your present anxiety?

HUSBAND: Yes, it has. The trouble we had brought us close together—my wife and I, that is. And then I have been more active in the church, so I feel that whatever happens, there has been some good in it.

The husband and wife had already had a tremendous crisis which had tested their faith. This was a secure rock of experience upon which they could anchor themselves during this new trial. By encouraging the husband to speak of his own religious experience, the nurse reinforced his faith.

There are many other principles which apply to the nurse's conversation with a patient about religion, but these four have been selected and illustrated for her general use:

(1) Listen to what the patient actually says.

(2) Be sensitive to the emotional tone of the conversation the patient offers.

(3) Respond in ways that will help the patient to see his problem more clearly, and help him to find alternatives which will bring a better solution.

(4) Encourage and build upon the religious convictions and faith which the patient already possesses.

If the nurse would like to know more about religious conversations with the patient, she will find additional instruction in chapters two and three of *Nurse, Pastor and Patient* by Granger Westburg.[1]

---

[1] Rock Island, Ill.: Augustana Press, 1955.

The Bible in Nursing Care

A general rule in medicine applies also to the Bible in nursing care. It is the accepted dictum that diagnosis precedes prescription. Both patients and nurses expect physical medication to be prescribed only after careful diagnosis, but they sometimes fail to recognize the need for a spiritual diagnosis before biblical passages are prescribed.

A student nurse noticed that one of her patients had a Gideon Bible by his bed. When she asked him where he was reading in the Bible, the patient replied, "Oh, I am just starting from the beginning." The nurse told him that she had been studying the Bible for many years and knew that it was not the easiest book to read and understand. But she felt that it always gave her something that she needed, and she was sure that it would do the same for him. Afterwards the nurse said that the patient made very few comments and appeared quite uninterested.

The nurse was observant and interested in the patient, but she did not relate the Bible to any specific problem of his. If she had said, "Perhaps you are looking for something in the Bible that would meet some special need of yours while you are in the hospital," the patient might have stated a specific concern. If the nurse knew of biblical passages that would speak to this need, she would demonstrate the relevance of the Scriptures for his life situation.

Some passages of Scripture that speak to specific problems of illness are these:

The night before an operation.—Rest and a quiet sense of confidence are essential for the patient at this time. Psalm 4:8 expresses the need of a patient: "In peace I will both lie down and sleep; for thou alone, O Lord, makest me dwell in safety."

The patient may be conscious of his weakness and need the reassurance of a verse like 2 Corinthians 12:9: "My grace is sufficient for you, for my power is made perfect in weakness."

For the general medical patient.—The medical patient may be a prey to many fears. Although great strides have been made in combating the spread of infection, comparatively little has been done to counteract the eroding effects of anxiety. For the patient with vague complaints who needs to conquer fears, some of the following verses may be appropriate:

I sought the Lord, and he answered me, and delivered me from all my fears (Psalm 34:4).

Commit your way to the Lord; trust in him, and he will act. . . . Be still before the Lord, and wait patiently for him (Psalm 37:5, 7).

I believe that I shall see the goodness of the Lord in the land of the living! Wait for the Lord; be strong, and let your heart take courage; yea, wait for the Lord! (Psalm 27:13–14, AV).

Come to me, all who labor and are heavy-laden, and I will give you rest (Matt. 11:28).

Cast all your anxieties on him, for he cares about you (1 Peter 5:7).

I sought the Lord, and he answered me, and delivered me from all my fears (Psalm 34:4).

The Lord is my light and salvation; whom shall I fear? The Lord is the stronghold of my life; of whom shall I be afraid? (Psalm 27:1).

For the chronically ill patient.—Patience is of special importance to those who will be ill a long time. Discouragement or cynicism may creep in. At such a time these verses may speak to the condition:

Wherefore seeing we also are compassed about with so great a cloud of witnesses, let us lay aside every weight, and the sin which doth so easily beset us, and let us run with patience the race that is set before us, looking unto Jesus the author and finisher of our faith; who for the joy that was set before him endured the cross, despising the shame, and is set down at the right hand of the throne of God (Heb. 12:1–2, AV).

Wherefore lift up the hands which hang down, and the feeble knees; and make straight paths for your feet, lest that which is lame be turned out of the way; but let it rather be healed. Follow peace with all men, and holiness, without which no man shall see the Lord:

looking diligently lest any man fail of the grace of God; lest any root of bitterness springing up trouble you, and thereby many be defiled (Heb. 12:12–15, AV).

Even the youths shall faint and be weary, and the young men shall utterly fall: but they that wait upon the Lord shall renew their strength; they shall mount up with wings as eagles; they shall run, and not be weary; and they shall walk, and not faint (Isa. 40:30–31, AV).

For the patient who is approaching death.—This Psalm is appropriate:

The Lord is my shepherd; I shall not want.
He maketh me to lie down in green pastures: he leadeth me beside the still waters.
He restoreth my soul: he leadeth me in the paths of righteousness for his name's sake.
Yea, though I walk through the valley of the shadow of death, I will fear no evil: for thou art with me; thy rod and thy staff they comfort me.
Thou preparest a table before me in the presence of mine enemies: thou anointest my head with oil; my cup runneth over.
Surely goodness and mercy shall follow me all the days of my life: and I will dwell in the house of the Lord for ever (Psalm 23, AV).

Some other meaningful passages at this significant time are: Psalm 90:1–4; Psalm 121; John 14:1–7, 25–27; Romans 8:31–39; 2 Corinthians 5; Revelation 21:1–4.

For the patient who feels guilty.—When a patient's guilt is based upon reality and he wants forgiveness, he may seek it from God as well as from men. The nurse can reassure him with this verse: "If we confess our sins, he is faithful and just, and will forgive our sins and cleanse us from all unrighteousness" (1 John 1:9). If the patient continues to be unsure of forgiveness and to say, "But I cannot forgive myself," the nurse might read 1 John 3:19–20: "And hereby we know that we are of the truth, and shall assure our hearts before him. For if our heart condemn us, God is greater than our heart, and knoweth all things" (AV). There is also the assurance of Isaiah 1:18: "Come now, and let us reason together, saith the Lord: though your sins be as scarlet, they shall be as white as snow; though they be red like crimson, they shall be as wool" (AV).

In all of the previous suggestions the biblical selections have been presented as a source of comfort and strength. Occasionally a nurse will meet a patient who regards the Bible as a book of law from which he assumes authority to act as a judge of other people. He may seek to lead the nurse into an argument about religion. The nurse should not enter into such a discussion any more than she would argue about the merits of various medicines. If a patient wishes to press some point of religion, the nurse may say, "I know that religion can mean a great deal to people, and I want you to have the best help available with the questions that you have raised. Because of your interest in religion, I would like very much for our chaplain to talk with you. Would you like for me to ask him to call?" If the patient is insistent and continues to press his opinions, the nurse may say that he should talk this over with his minister, priest, or rabbi, just as she would refer him to his doctor if he objected to some medicine which was prescribed.

In conclusion it should be noted that convalescent patients may do a good deal of reading. The American Bible Society has an illustrated edition of all the books of the New Testament. These may be obtained for patients separately or as an entire New Testament by the chaplain or some church organization. The Revised Standard Version is best for most patients, since it is clear and accurate. Some Protestant patients prefer the King James' Version, and the nurse will find that most Gideon Bibles which are supplied in hospitals are of that version. Catholic patients have been encouraged by the Pope to read the Bible, although they are permitted to read only official Roman translations, such as the Douay translation. Devout Jews will probably bring their own copy of the Hebrew Scriptures and a prayer book. If not, most departments of religion or a local synagogue will be able to furnish a copy for the patient if he makes known his desire to have one.

Additional Scripture verses are listed on pages 109–11 of *Who*

Is My Patient? by Russell L. Dicks [2] and pages 52–54 of *Nurse, Pastor and Patient* by Chaplain Granger Westberg.[3] *Grace Sufficient* by Wayne Oates [4] contains Scripture verses which are organized under appropriate headings for those who are sick or distressed. If a nurse wishes to read further into the use of the Bible in nursing care, she will be profited by reading *The Bible and Pastoral Care* by Wayne Oates.[5]

Prayer for the Sick

Prayer is one of the chief spiritual antidotes for fear, bitterness, morbid obsessions of guilt, loneliness, and boredom. It is the channel through which men express thanks to God and make known their requests to him. Prayer is most often thought of as spoken words, but it also involves the unseen Spirit of Christ who intercedes with expression too deep for words.[6]

The nurse's attitude toward the patient and her personal estimation of prayer will in large measure determine the use of prayer in the sickroom. A confident, compassionate attitude on the part of the nurse will lead many patients to request her prayers. A cool, aloof, or nervous nurse will probably receive no requests.

Patients' requests for prayer in the hospital usually arise in crises, such as: the night before or the morning of an operation; in lucid moments amidst a critical illness; during a night of worry or intermittent pain; when a patient feels guilty but is blocked from praying by disuse, hostility, or bitterness.

The nurse's prayer for the patient should be a spiritual prescription which fits a need. Usually the patient will tell the nurse why prayer is desired. If there is any doubt, the nurse may say, "I will be glad to pray with you. What is it that you want to pray for?" Once the nurse is apprised of the patient's need, she should relax for a moment, remembering to ask for God's presence before she prays. Then she may offer a brief prayer which

[2] New York: The Macmillan Company, 1941.
[3] Rock Island, Ill.: Augustana Book Concern, 1955.
[4] Nashville: Broadman Press, 1951.
[5] Philadelphia: Westminster Press, 1953.
[6] Rom. 8:26.

consists of a few sentences. The prayer should thank God for his presence and for the promise of spiritual strength. Any specific request of the patient should be mentioned. Roman Catholics, Lutherans, Episcopalians, and Jews may have their prayer books with them and ask the nurse to read them a prayer. After the brief prayer, it is good to leave the room without further remarks so that the patient may meditate. If the prayer has awakened thoughts he wants to discuss further, he will ask her to remain a moment.

In many denominational hospitals there are small booklets which contain daily devotions. Usually a Scripture verse and a prayer are included in each of these. If the patient does not already have one, the nurse may request it from the department of religion. Excellent examples of pastoral prayers may be found in *Nurse, Pastor and Patient*, pages 82–90; *Springs of Living Water* by Carl Scherzer;[7] *Who Is My Patient?* pages 117–41; and in two other books by Russell Dicks, *My Faith Looks Up*[8] and *Thy Health Shall Spring Forth*.[9] These references contain prayers for Catholic, Protestant, and Jewish patients.

Children and Religion

The Bible and prayer may be very meaningful for children who come from Christian or Jewish homes. Children have many questions about God, the world, and all the why's of life. Nurses answer these informally on duty and sometimes formally as Sunday school teachers on children's units in hospitals. Few books are available which explain the religious world of children to nurses and parents. The following, however, are excellent:

TRENT, ROBBIE. *Your Child and God.* New York: Harper & Brothers, 1952.

WHITEHOUR, ELIZABETH. *The Children We Teach.* Philadelphia: Judson Press, 1950.

YEAXLEE, BASIL A. *Religion and the Growing Mind.* Greenwich, Conn.: Seabury Press, 1952.

---

[7] Philadelphia: Westminster Press, 1951.

[8] Philadelphia: Westminster Press, 1949.

[9] New York: The Macmillan Company, 1950.

The special world of illness is interpreted for parents in *You and Your Child's Health* by Paulette K. Hartrich.[10] This is a book to be given to the parents of a child prior to his entrance as a patient in a hospital or during illness. When the child is ready to go home, or when brought to the out-patient clinic and told to stay in bed, a book recommended for parents is *Caring for the Sick Child at Home* by Marion Lowndes.[11]

The philosophy and technics of teaching religion will be found in the literature of each denomination. Excellent guidance is given in three manuals of the Board of Education of the Presbyterian Church, USA: *When We Teach Kindergarten Children* by Kathrene M. Tobey; *When We Teach Primary Children* by Marjorie Haynes; and *When We Teach Junior Children* by Jane B. Harris.

There are several books about the Bible and prayer which nurses may read to children. *Small Rain* by Jessie Jones[12] has full-page drawings of children at the seashore, in the meadow, and at other play. Under each drawing is an appropriate Scripture passage. *A Child's Grace*[13] uses lively photographs of children to illustrate the verses of a prayer by E. R. Leatham. Any of these may be used both at mealtime or at bedtime.

Books that may be given to children include the following:

For the preschool child:

Bruce, Mary Owen. *Once, Long Ago.* Philadelphia: Westminster Press, 1948.

Davis, Sadie H. *Jesus Once a Child.* Nashville: Broadman Press, 1954.

Trent, Robbie. *A Star Shone.* Philadelphia: Westminster Press, 1948.

For children 6 to 8:

Jones, Mary Alice. *Bible Stories.* New York: Rand McNally, 1952.

———. *The Ten Commandments.* New York: Rand McNally, 1956.

---

[10] New York: Harper & Brothers, 1955.
[11] Philadelphia: Westminster Press, 1955.
[12] New York: Viking Press, 1943.
[13] New York: E. P. Dutton, 1948.

TRENT, ROBBIE. *Always There Is God.* New York: Abingdon-Cokesbury Press, 1950.

———. *I Can Tell God Things.* Nashville: Broadman Press, 1954.

———. *The Little Old Lady.* Nashville: Broadman Press, 1958.

For children 9 to 12:

NIEDERMEYER, MABEL. *Some Time Every Day.* St. Louis: Bethany Press, 1948.

TRENT, ROBBIE. *Daily Discoveries.* New York: Harper & Brothers, 1955.

The Limitations of a Nurse's Religious Ministry

After reading all of these suggestions concerning a religious ministry, a nurse may wonder whether or not she can do all of these things. Lest she become discouraged, it should be said that she can do a great deal. And before anyone is overwhelmed by the magnitude of the task, it will be well to consider some limitations of the religious ministry of a nurse.

One of the first limitations is related to the nurse's training. She will, most likely, have a better understanding of the personality and the spiritual problems of illness than most people of her age. But she is not expected to be an expert in pastoral counseling. It is therefore important for her to know when to turn to the chaplain or a pastor. This is one of the problems which will be considered in the next chapter.

A second limitation concerns the nurse's role in the hospital. She is a representative of the medical community. She may be deeply religious and communicate this very effectively to her patients. But her primary function is that of a nurse. If she is ineffective in her professional work, it does not matter how pious or sincere she may be in her religion. Her primary duty is to be a good nurse. Religion is no substitute for professional competence. Therefore, the nurse who neglects her studies to attend religious meetings or pretends that her prayers are more important than an orderly schedule of learning only deceives herself. Nursing is her profession, her God-given opportunity to prepare for service. Whether she ever speaks a specific word about religion or not, she has ministered as God's servant when she performs her nursing duties faithfully.

The nurse symbolizes a medical community. She does not stand for any particular denomination unless she wears a religious habit such as a nun or a deaconess. Questions about particular denominations are better left to the designated and trained representatives of those groups, who are pastors, priests, or rabbis. Also, these latter persons are the specific symbolic representatives of God. Although the nurse may stand as God's representative to many patients on many occasions, this is not her unique symbolic role in the hospital. The differences between the role of a nurse and that of a pastor will be discussed in the following chapter.

A third limiting factor is psychological. Many patients look to a nurse as they would look to a mother. The nurse is expected to be gentle, sympathetic, and understanding, just as an ideal mother would be. The nurse's religious ministry will therefore emphasize love, understanding, and forgiveness because these are appropriate to her work with patients.

10. The Nurse and the Pastor

EARLY IN THIS BOOK it was pointed out that body and soul cannot be absolutely separated from one another. Likewise, it cannot be said that the nurse works only with the body and that the pastor ministers only to the soul. The nurse may be as concerned about religion as the pastor, and the pastor as interested in the patient's health as the nurse. But there are some obvious differences. These are related to the various functions of the nurse and the pastor and do not imply any judgment of their basic religious commitments.

The different roles of the nurse and the pastor have been discussed in a previous chapter. The nurse represents a medical community. The pastor represents a specific religious community. The clergyman is a representative of God and the church, and his words and actions carry spiritual authority which is recognized. The nurse's religious authority is dependent upon her personality and her ability to communicate with the patient.

A second difference between pastor and nurse is related to the length of time a pastor and a nurse know a patient. Except in some small-town hospitals, a nurse probably has not seen the patient previously and may not see him after he leaves the hospital. But the pastor is presumed to have some acquaintance with the patient who is a member of his congregation. When the pastor visits him in the hospital, the patient may brighten because the minister is one who knows everyone whom he knows in the community back home. If the pastor has officiated at his wedding or baptized his children, the visit will be even more meaningful. In many and varied ways the pastor brings happy and unhappy memories from the person's background. In addition, the pastor will probably see the patient after he leaves the hospital. If he cannot speak about many matters while the patient is seriously ill, he can bide his time until the patient is at home and convalescing. When the doctor has said that the patient must change his way of life if he is to get well, it is the pastor who will see him in the months and years ahead to discuss the ways by which he will orient himself to a new life.

In contrast, the nurse does what she can in a period of three to seven days, if she works in a general hospital. In a convalescent unit or in a psychiatric department the time of her contact with the patient may be extended to months and perhaps years. Yet the nurse sees the patient primarily within a medical setting.[1] Her knowledge of the patient before he entered the hospital and after he leaves is quite limited. Therefore, if a nurse has had significant religious conversations with the patient and hopes that someone will continue these after he has returned to his home, she should notify the pastor of his local church. Her responsibility is within the hospital or other similar setting. The pastor works both within and outside the medical community.

A final distinction between the concerns of a nurse and pastor is in regard to illness and health. A nurse usually sees patients only when they are sick. If she should be recognized by a former patient on the street, the former patient may be eager to let the nurse know that he is now well and should not be considered a sick person. The intimate, personal relationship between the nurse and patient is a temporary one that is usually bounded by the beginning and the ending of sickness.

But a pastor has a ministry to persons both in illness and in health. He may call upon his parishioners when they are sick and when they are healthy. It is not expected of a nurse or doctor to call when patients have fully recovered, because people usually have contact with hospital persons only for the duration of an

[1] The public health nurse works outside the hospital and has much information about the family, but she is still a representative of the medical community.

illness. Even the public health nurse, who operates in the community and among healthy persons more than most nurses, does not call routinely upon all the persons in the neighborhood in the same way that a pastor does.[2]

Basic Courtesies between Nurses and Ministers

Although the functions of the nurse and the pastor differ, they are both concerned about the same patient. A harmonious relationship between them will be of great advantage to the patient's health. There is a mutual responsibility for courtesy and encouragement.

One of the first contacts between nurse and pastor occurs at the nurses' station on each unit. A pastor who is in a hospital should always stop at the nurses' station to identify himself. If a nurse observes a well-dressed stranger who she thinks is a clergyman and who makes frequent visits to patients on her ward, she might graciously ask him if he is a pastor. She might then suggest that he stop at the nurses' station before he leaves and introduce himself in order that the other nurses might have an opportunity to meet him. She might also suggest that they would be pleased to offer him any courtesy or assistance.

When a pastor does identify himself at the nurses' station, he will usually say that he wishes to visit a certain patient and ask if it is all right. If the minister indicates that the patient is a stranger to him, the nurse should offer to introduce him to the patient. This is especially helpful in a four-bed ward or semi-private room, where the pastor may not recognize his parishioner. If the pastor does know his parishioner and the nurse knows that the pastor is a competent person, she may tell him whatever she thinks will be helpful about the patient's condition. If she is not acquainted with the pastor or knows from a previous experience that he is an impulsive and ill-trained person, she will probably only give information about the amount of time doctors say visitors should stay in the room.

---

[2] The patient's acceptance of the public health nurse is discussed in chapter 2 of *The Public Health Nurse and Her Patient* by Ruth Gilbert (Cambridge, Mass.: Harvard University Press, 1951).

When a pastor tells the nurse whom he is visiting, she can protect his privacy with the patient by notifying other personnel that the pastor is in the room. A nurse can always be helpful to a clergyman by giving him as much privacy as possible with a patient. If food or medication is immediately necessary, the nurse may ask the minister before he enters the room if he can delay his visit for a few moments. Since his time is precious, she should tell him immediately when the patient is ready to receive him.

The business of food and medication is quite important. It is most disconcerting for a pastor in the midst of a crucial discussion with his parishioner to be suddenly interrupted by a nurse who opens the door and cheerfully announces that Mrs. Johnson's shot is ready. It is also a matter for righteous indignation when a minister is about to pray with a patient and a maid bursts into a room with a lunch tray in hand. If the minister has not told anyone where he is, he is responsible for the blunder. If he has informed the nurse of his presence, it is her responsibility to protect this privacy.

On occasion a nurse may think that a pastor has disturbed a patient. If there is a chaplain in the hospital, she should tell him. The chaplain may call the minister and find that the patient needed to have a good cry because of a delayed grief reaction. The chaplain may visit the patient himself to discover what the trouble was, or he may relay this information to the doctor. After the pastoral therapy is understood, some directions may be given to the nurse which will help her in her care of the patient. If after careful investigation it is found that a pastor does disturb a patient unduly, the doctor should consult with the pastor about it. However, such incidents are extremely rare.

When to Call for a Chaplain or Pastor

Chaplain Westberg has listed nine types of patients who respond best to pastoral care. These are as follows: (1) One who is lonely and has few, if any, visitors. (2) One who expresses some apprehensions and fears. (3) One whose illness may have some connection with his emotions or with his religious attitudes. (4) One who is facing surgery. (5) One whose surgery or illness forces him to change his way of living, such as cardiac patients, amputees, and patients with colostomies. (6) One who seems to be doing more than the average amount of thinking about the relationship of his religion to his health. (7) One whose pastor is unable to call on him or who has no church affiliation and consequently would receive no pastoral care. (8) One whose illness has obvious social implications, such as an unwed mother or those with difficult home problems. (9) One whose illness is terminal.[3]

How to Contact Ministers

When there is a chaplain in the hospital, the nurse may call or page him to notify that he is needed in a certain room because the family requests a visit or the patient has suddenly become critical and the family is disturbed.

When no chaplain is available, the problem is more complicated. When the relatives request a visit from a minister, the nurse should ask them about the patient's religion. The nurse's own pastor may be a wonderful man, but he may not be of the denomination that is preferred by this family. There also may be a problem between the patient and his relatives concerning religion. For example, the patient may have listed "Baptist" on his admission card while his wife steadfastly protests that *her* minister, of another denomination, should be called. The nurse should not try to choose between the two; let the couple decide. The nurse has fulfilled her obligation if she has reminded them to call a minister. The selection of a minister is the patient's privilege.

If a patient or relative asks for a priest or a Protestant minister, then a nurse may do one of several things. When the patient is Roman Catholic and there is no hospital chaplain, she may notify the priest who is assigned as the hospital visitor by the diocese. If she does not know his name, a head nurse or someone in the administrative office will know. Or the nurse may look in the telephone book for the name of the Catholic church which

---

[3] *Op. cit.*, p. 73.

is nearest to the hospital and tell the family to call there for information.

For a Protestant patient who has no church affiliation the procedure will depend somewhat upon the size of the city. In a smaller town one or more Protestant ministers may be known for their interest in a ministry to the sick. Usually one of these pastors is called when a patient requests a visit from a pastor. In larger cities a minister is often designated by the ministerial association as "chaplain of the week." Each Protestant pastor takes his turn as volunteer chaplain for one week. Notice of this is usually given to the administrative office of the hospital, and the nurse can advise the family of the name of the pastor who is the chaplain at that time. In many cities there will be a council of churches which can supply information on Protestant ministers who are available for hospital calls. The council of churches will be listed in the telephone book. In larger cities individual denominations may maintain a staff of chaplains. For example, in Houston, Texas, a Baptist patient who wished to be visited by a Baptist pastor could call the Union Baptist Association, and one of the chaplains of the association would visit him within a day.

Whenever possible the nurse will encourage the relatives to make their own decision about the person whom they wish to visit in the name of religion. For more information on referring patients and families to pastors and other sources of strength *Where to Go for Help* by Wayne Oates [4] is recommended.

Co-operation with a Chaplain

There are many hospitals in the United States that employ chaplains. A chaplain's ministry may be quite varied. If, for example, there is only one chaplain for a five-hundred-bed hospital, he may do little more than greet patients. If a staff of chaplains is available through a department of religion, a nurse may be assured of better religious service and be encouraged to work more actively with the chaplains in their ministry.

One of the best ways that a nurse may work with a chaplain

---

[4] Philadelphia: Westminster Press, 1957.

is to sense the spiritual needs of her patients, such as those listed previously. She may tell the chaplain about them when he is visiting on her floor. She may also encourage patients to ask for the chaplain.

Some patients need to know what a chaplain is and what he does. The chaplain, like the pastor, is a representative of God and the church. Usually he is one who has been trained to understand patients' feelings and to interpret their experiences to them. The unique function of the chaplain is to give a religious interpretation to these experiences and to help the patient discover spiritual resources with which he may face the problems of fear, anxiety, distrust, guilt, or loneliness.

The functions of the chaplain's department may be divided in several categories: (1) pastoral care, (2) communication with the pastors and churches, (3) religious consultation, and (4) teaching.

Patients will be most interested in the first of these functions, pastoral care. If they are members of a local congregation, they should expect their pastor rather than the hospital chaplain to visit them. The chaplain is a pastor to patients away from home or patients who have no church affiliation. These are the persons who have priority on his time, since no other minister in the community has responsibility for them.

A second function, communication, is important to patients before they enter the hospital. Chaplains often speak to civic and church organizations about religion and medicine. This is one of the ways in which people learn about the medical community and are reassured that their personal needs will be met if they should ever enter a hospital.

Communication is also a service to local clergymen. Many departments of religion have secretaries who notify pastors when members of their churches are in the hospital. This is greatly appreciated because many families neglect to inform their minister when a person enters a hospital. When a pastor has been notified and arrives at the hospital, he may desire additional help in communication from the chaplain; he may wish to meet a patient's doctor or discuss a nursing or administrative problem.

The chaplain can introduce him to the appropriate doctor, nurse, or administrator.

This liaison activity of the chaplain not only prepares patients for their hospital experience, but it also prevents potential friction by bringing pastors and hospital personnel face to face. In personal conversation they can dispel many doubts about personnel and clarify misinterpretations of hospital procedures.

A third function of the chaplain is consultation. This is a service to pastors who visit patients and to nurses and doctors of patients in the hospital. A minister may be puzzled by the attitudes of a parishioner. He may wonder how to approach complex problems, such as those of a person who has attempted suicide. The chaplain's specialized training and practice will be helpful to the pastor who asks for consultation.

Nurses and doctors may seek out the chaplain for advice about the religious problems of patients or about their own spiritual difficulties. As a pastor, he is conscience-bound to respect any private conversation as a confidence.

A fourth function of the chaplain is teaching. Some chaplains have graduate degrees in theology and have taken special courses which equip them to train pastors and theological students in the hospital. Many hospitals request the chaplain to hold seminars for head nurses and supervisors and to teach classes on religion to student nurses.

The Nurse and the Sacraments

A major spiritual resource in some denominations is the sacramental ministry. Roman Catholics, Episcopalians, Lutherans, and several other denominations give much attention to the sacraments, which are the outward and visible signs of inner spiritual grace. The ministry of the sacraments is not stressed in some other denominations, such as the Baptist, the Nazarene, and the Assembly of God. Methodists and Presbyterians make some use of the sacraments, such as bedside communion for the sick, but do not lay such important stress upon them as do the Roman Catholics, Missouri Synod Lutherans, or the Episcopalians.

Two sacraments—baptism and communion—are recognized

by most denominations. A third sacrament, extreme unction, is important to Catholic and some Episcopalian patients. The nurse is required to notify the family or the Roman Catholic church whenever a Roman Catholic patient is in danger of death so that the priest may come to anoint designated parts of the body with oil and say special prayers. Extreme unction can be administered only once during a serious illness. The nurse should not remain in the room during this rite, and no special preparation other than tidying up the room or drawing the curtains in a ward is necessary.

The nurse is more directly involved in baptism and communion. Since the discussion of the nurse's role in baptism will be presented later, only communion will be presented here.

Chaplain Westberg has stressed the importance of communion for all patients who look to it for spiritual strength. He speaks against the common belief that communion is only for the dying. While it may serve as a last rite, communion also provides comfort and strength for patients on many occasions, such as the night before an operation or during convalescence. A nurse can often help a patient to understand this. An Episcopal patient told his nurse, "I am sorry that I cannot go to chapel this morning. I would love to take communion." The nurse replied, "Would you like for me to call your minister so that he may come and give you communion?"

When a patient requests communion, it is important for the nurse to ask the patient, the patient's family, or the pastor to let her know when the communion is to be observed. She will want to prepare the room for the coming of the priest or the minister. Her first duty is to see that the room is tidy. The second is to spread a clean white cloth over any flat surface, such as a dresser or a night table. Chaplain Westberg suggests that for Lutheran patients it is well to arrange a bedside table at the foot of the bed so that the pastor may face the parishioner as he performs the service. For Catholic patients, the dresser or table should be cleared and placed some distance from the patient. If possible, the patient should be in a sitting position in the bed. The nurse should not remain in the room during the administration of the sacrament unless the physical condition of the patient makes it necessary or the clergyman asks her.

Catholic patients may not take solid food for three hours preceding Holy Communion except by special permission. Water and medicines may be taken at any time. Liquids other than water may be taken until one hour prior to communion. If a priest or pastor delays his coming long past the time of breakfast for a patient, the nurse may consult the chaplain, or she may call the pastor or priest. If there is an unavoidable delay, the patient should be informed.

Once a priest has entered the room of a Roman Catholic patient to administer communion, the nurse should be careful to guard his privacy, because confession and penance are sometimes part of the preparation for communion. In a hospital ward the nurse may screen the patient's bed.

This privacy may not be desired or useful for a Methodist or Presbyterian patient who is receiving communion. Instead, his reception of communion may be an experience which the entire ward can witness and benefit from. The nurse may therefore ask the patient and the pastor if this is to be a private service or a service which others may watch.

Since the teaching concerning communion will vary from one denomination to another, the nurse should know the denomination of her chaplain. A Southern Baptist chaplain, for example, would not administer communion anywhere other than in a church because he believes this is an ordinance of the church which is to be observed by the entire fellowship. But he would be happy to find a pastor of the patient's denomination who will administer the sacrament privately. Therefore, instead of saying to a patient who asks for communion, "Why, no, our chaplain does not do that kind of thing," the nurse should say, "I will notify the chaplain's office; he will see that someone comes to serve you."

Jewish Observances

Laws of fasting which are important to Catholics, Eastern Orthodox, and Jewish patients are not obligatory upon the sick.

Many patients who belong to these religious groups may voluntarily seek to observe dietary regulations while they are in the hospital, but when health or ability to work would be seriously affected, they are exempt from these religious duties. Reform and Conservative Jews will be more liberal at this point. Orthodox Jews may be very strict. These patients often need the reassurance of their rabbi about breaking dietary laws upon medical orders. Older persons may be hard to convince.

There is one belief of Orthodox Jews which must be closely respected by hospital personnel; only members of the "Sacred Brotherhood" of the Orthodox Synagogue may prepare the body for burial. No one else is to touch the body after the spirit departs. Orthodox Jews are forbidden to allow an autopsy.

This would not be true in all Jewish groups. The chairman of the Rabbinical Council of the East Coast, Rabbi Nathan Drazin, informed student nurses at Johns Hopkins Hospital that "autopsies and embalming are permitted only under special emergencies; for example, autopsies may be permitted when we know of another patient who is suffering from a similar disease, whose life is endangered, and who may be saved by this post-mortem examination. Jewish law does allow the abrogation of all its ordinances for the possible direct saving of a human life, excepting only the following three—murder, adultery, and blasphemy." [5]

For additional information on the nurse's ministry to different denominations see chapter six and the appendix in *Nurse, Pastor and Patient* and *Religious Care for Hospital Patients*, a pamphlet available from Chaplain Malcolm Ballinger of the University Hospital, Ann Arbor, Michigan.

---

[5] Letter to author from Chaplain Leslie Weber, July 31, 1958.

11. The Ethics of Interpersonal Relationships

HEBREW-CHRISTIAN ETHICS are concerned with personal relationships because God is personal. In the Old Testament his commands begin with the personal pronoun "thou": "Thou shalt . . ."[1] The Lord God required both individual and group loyalty to his covenant in those whom he called to be his servants. In the New Testament, God demonstrated his love for men by sending his only Son to earth for their salvation.[2] Jesus commanded his disciples to love one another as God loved them.[3] One of his disciples stated quite bluntly: "If any one says, 'I love God,' and hates his brother, he is a liar; for he who does not love his brother whom he has seen, cannot love God whom he has not seen. And this commandment we have from him, that he who loves God should love his brother also."[4]

The basic ethics of the Bible are personal.[5] Slavish conformity to ritual or salvation through good works is condemned.[6] Men are saved by trust in God rather than through the merits of their own righteousness.[7]

Biblical emphasis upon an "I–Thou" relationship, that is, a heart-to-heart communication with other human beings, is dif-

[1] Ex. 20:3–17; Deut. 6:4–9.
[2] John 3:16–21.
[3] John 15:12–17.
[4] 1 John 4:20–21.
[5] Mic. 6:8.
[6] Matt. 23:1–36; 1 Cor. 13:1–3; Rom. 3:19–20.
[7] Deut. 7:6–11; Rom. 1:17; 3:21–26.

ferent from conventional American morality. In our culture there is "religious" sanction for an "I–It" relationship. Instead of appraising a neighbor as a person for whom Christ died, many people stamp a label on him and regard him as an "It." A person who lives "on the other side of town" may be an "It" who can be ignored at school or snubbed on social occasions. A Negro is stamped as an "It" by many people who justify their hatred, fear, and pride through the blasphemy that God has made one race inferior to another. An instructor or head nurse may be an "It" to many students if they identify her with some authority in the past who was bigoted, insensitive, or hard to please.

Distinctive Principles of Christian Ethics

Love for God and neighbor, or an "I–Thou" relationship toward God and man, is a basic principle of Christian ethics. It is based upon the revealed nature of God as One who cares for man. The ultimate criteria of Christian morality is faithfulness to Christ. Personal relationships are to embody the quality of his way of life.

Certain characteristics of Christian morality follow from the desire to pattern human life after that of Jesus.[8]

(1) The Christian ethic is a divine imperative, revealed by God himself. The importance of moral conduct is based upon the knowledge that God cares for men. Because he loves them, the imperative is that they should love one another. The source of Christian morality is the loving character of God, for both the power to attain and the model come from One greater than man.

(2) The Christian ethic is an inward morality. Christ calls for faith and obedience in which love is the supreme motive. The Christian is inner-directed rather than outwardly motivated, for faith in Christ gives him a new focus of loyalty. The image of God within is perfected through the indwelling Spirit of Christ. This should not encourage morbid introspection or a selfish desire to do good with an eye to personal rewards.

---

[8] This material is based on a reading of Harold Titus, *What Is Morality?* (New York: The Macmillan Company, 1943).

(3) The inner Christ motivates an outer concern for all mankind. The Christian feels personally responsible for the welfare of the "little ones," the insignificant, and the neglected as well as for the stigmatized members of society. A ministry to one of these is a service to Christ.

(4) The Christian ideal is embodied and exemplified in a person, Jesus Christ. His life was in perfect harmony with what he taught. Sincerity and love, urgency and patience, and strength and tenderness were balanced in him. He was true God in the person of a man, unique in history.

(5) The continual sustenance of Christian morality is the Holy Spirit. This Spirit, dwelling in the hearts of believers, is willing to do for believers today everything that Jesus did for the early disciples. Through this indwelling Spirit, God is real to man.

(6) The Christian ethic is always related to the Christian fellowship, which is the church. The apostle Paul reminded the Ephesian congregation that they were no longer strangers or wanderers upon earth but fellow citizens with other saints in God's kingdom. Living with Christ as the Head of the church body, they were to fit in with each other, just as different parts of the physical body function together.[9] Paul then described the worthy Christian life as a loving relationship between children and parents, wives and husbands, and employees and employers.[10] When a Christian tries to lead a worthy life apart from the fellowship of believers, his action must be caused by a misunderstanding, a disillusioning experience, or ignorance.

(7) Duty and hope are balanced in the Christian ethic. The Christian is always striving for a better society and a purer personal life. But he does not neglect his daily tasks merely because good and evil are mixed in his mundane affairs. A student may be disillusioned by some things, but this does not justify a rejection of the church, Christian morality, or a high level of professional responsibility. The Christian strives to walk worthily in this world even while he longs for a better one.

With these distinctive principles in mind, the next step is to do

---

[9] Eph. 2, 4.

[10] Eph. 4–6.

two things. First, some specific directives concerning an area of ethics which is of special concern to student nurses will be presented. These will be the marks of mature morality. Since students and instructors will be vitally concerned with the problems of maturation during nurses' training, this section deserves special attention.

Second, interpersonal relationships with the patient's family need to be considered, as well as relations with other professional persons and patients. These will be considered in terms of mature morality and the way in which people relate to each other as a "Thou" rather than as an "It."

The Marks of Mature Morality

Maturity implies an organization of self around a worthy center of loyalty which, for the Christian, is Jesus Christ. Since maturity is a process, the morality of an act or attitude must be judged in terms of personal development. A freshman may be highly critical of all students who do not act as she does. This may be her first experience in a new environment. She evaluates people exactly as her parents judged people at home.

By the time she is a graduate nurse, this girl, it is hoped, will have learned to judge people in the light of *their* circumstances. She should have grown enough to understand why some people see things and do things differently from the people of her home town. The personal maturity of nursing education should enable her to apply universal moral principles to the particular problems of individuals.

The following ethical criteria are presented to aid nurses in the attainment of a mature morality.

A person is morally mature if he judges an act as right or wrong on the basis of its effect on persons or on human welfare. In persons only are there characteristics and qualities of supreme worth. The valid test of any institution or a system will be its effect on persons and the scope it gives for the development of personality.

A person is morally mature if he possesses a spirit of love or selflessness and, when necessary, self-sacrifice. Class conflict, racial pride, and personal selfishness are not overcome by natural moral disposition. Christianity teaches that love for others is based on the love of God.[11]

A morally mature person places a premium upon knowledge and intelligence. Often there is a desire to help people, but the know-how is lacking. This is zeal without knowledge. The morally mature person combines knowledge and intelligence with spiritual earnestness and enthusiasm.

A person is morally mature only when he can be motivated by inner rather than outer controls. People who are morally mature must learn to accept responsibility for their own conduct even though it may involve accepting blame. A nurse may discover privately that she has given the wrong medication to a patient. Even though she observes no alarming symptoms in him because of this, she still must report her error. Concern for her patient's welfare must come before the desire to escape blame and censure.

A mature person judges the entire act. Good motives, accepted means in carrying out the act, and wholesome consequences are all involved. A nurse may be tempted to immoral conduct because it would please her lover. Good will to men is a *part* of morality, but not all. When she judges the act more comprehensively, she will discover that the means are not acceptable. That is, sexual intercourse is not a responsible way to demonstrate affection before marriage. Furthermore, the consequences are heavy with worry and guilt. The girl has sacrificed future self-respect as a wife and mother to make present circumstances pleasant.

A mature person recognizes that for a better society there must be both transformed individuals and social reconstruction. On the one hand, selfish, unregenerate, narrow individuals may ruin any social system. In contrast, great social sins may destroy persons faster than they can be saved. The nurse therefore has a Christian responsibility both to give her individual witness and to participate in organizations which will conserve the best of the past and change society for the better.

---

[11] Rom. 7:21; 8:39.

A person is morally mature only when he is willing to grow with a changing world. The New Testament gives a moral tone but does not present specific directions about automobile driving, dating, dancing, or atomic armaments. These problems arise in new generations, and each must solve them on the basis of the moral tone of God's Word.

A mature person interprets human duties as duties to God and thus gives eternal significance to his moral life. To do good just because the individual will ultimately benefit from it is little more than enlightened selfishness. To be good because regional culture demands it is to be at the mercy of public opinion. Christian morality is based on neither of these. Instead, it springs from a new relation to God. And because it is founded upon a personal relationship with the eternal Creator, it is an absolute and universal ethic.

The Ethics of Professional Relationships

Christian morality involves more than one person. The man who loves God must love his neighbor also. Sometimes a nurse forgets this obvious principle with the people whom she sees the most—other nurses, doctors, and hospital personnel. Too often people set up images of what certain positions are like and squeeze people into these preconceived pigeon holes. Thus instead of looking upon a competent head nurse as a person with responsibility, some see only an "authority." Because of a previous unpleasant experience, "authority" may mean autocratic rule, punishment, or contempt for inferiors. With such an image in her mind, a student or nurse on duty may act in seemingly ridiculous ways toward a sensitive head nurse or supervisor. The student may resent any instruction and take any suggestion as a personal insult. Or she may run to the "authority" for every decision and seek to know the supervisor's opinion on anything before she will venture one of her own. Such behavior is not based upon a realistic relationship between two human beings but is the product of immature emotions that the student first developed toward a parent, a teacher, or an older sister.

The principal problem of the student nurse in this context is her relationship with authority. If the student can see the instructor, the head nurse, and the doctor as persons who take responsibility so that she may learn without getting hurt or hurting anyone else, she will accept them as persons. Students often mention the head nurse as a major factor in their early adjustment to nursing duties. One said, "As I went up the elevator on my first day of duty, I felt sick. But I calmed down quite a bit after I met my head nurse because she put me at ease immediately. She told me that I didn't need to be afraid because my patient wouldn't bite me." Another student said, "When it was time to transfer to surgery, my greatest fear concerned the nurses on that particular unit, for I wondered whether or not they would be as helpful as the graduates on medicine where I had worked. My first day the head nurse made us feel so relieved. She said that whenever we made a mistake or saw someone else making one, we should report it to her. She surely took up for us students in a way that made our work there a real joy."

In both these examples the student and the head nurse saw each other as persons, not as "students" and "authorities." Instead of relating coldly to an "It," they formed a warm human bond with another person, a "Thou." This is a basic principle of Christian ethics: that individuals look upon each other as persons rather than as things.

Another authority with whom the student nurse has contact is the doctor. The doctor has become a working partner with the nurse, although as an authority. Instead of "kidding the doctor along," nurses are beginning to relate to doctors as fellow professionals with a distinctive competence.[12] From an ethical point of view, this new type of relationship is highly desirable. Nurses no longer need to subdue an occasional rude or bullying doctor by spreading an unfavorable report about him throughout the hospital and "ganging up" on him in subtle ways. The supervisor may state her opinions openly to the doctor or administrator in the security of her professional role. This is in keeping with the

---

[12] Temple Burling *et al.*, *The Give and Take in Hospitals* (New York: G. P. Putnam's Sons, 1956), p. 88.

apostle Paul's admonition that Christians make an open declaration of the truth to all men.

In this changing relationship of doctor and nurse, the primary moral principle is the effect upon persons and the development of personality. When students see supervisors as persons rather than as an image of a past authority, they are growing into maturity. When nurses see doctors as people with excellent training and authority, the initiative of both professions is quickened for the benefit of the patient as well as the staff.

Where this atmosphere prevails, student nurses can speak directly to their instructor or head nurse about unprofessional conduct on the part of a doctor or other authority. For example, student nurses were discussing the jokes and language some of the doctors used. One nurse said, "There are times when I'm in the operating room with two surgeons who just love to tell jokes to each other. Some of them are pretty raw. I laugh to myself at the funny ones, but get sick at some of the others. Anyway, they're not telling the jokes to me, so I just do my work." Another nurse said, "I don't like to be around Dr. ____. He curses about everything I do. I never liked to be around people who were profane, and I can hardly stand it when he curses me. One day he asked why I was all thumbs. I said that part of it was because I was so upset by his cursing. He laughed and said I needed to grow up and get to really know some men. I told the head nurse that I couldn't work with him any more. When she asked why, I told her. Somebody straightened him out, because he never says anything to me any more."

There is a basic medical as well as moral principle in this—the principle of the patient's welfare. When the profanity of a staff member detracts from a nurse's skill with his patient, then the profanity is detrimental to the patient's welfare. Further, some men who are insecure as males (or women who are insecure as females) may seek to bolster their egos by cursing or bragging about sexual knowledge. But when this inadequate form of compensation is used in the sick room as well as in the cocktail lounge, a person needs to be reminded by someone in authority of his responsibilities as a professional person.

The nurses made a distinction between offensive language directed at them and at other people. The nurse could choose to ignore jokes (the unfunny ones) which the doctors told each other. The nurse who was directly cursed by the doctor had to do something because her basic integrity was abused.

The Ethics of Nurse-Patient Relationships

A basic ethical issue in nurse-patient relationships is the concern on the part of the nurse for the personality of her patient. The patient is a "Thou" rather than an "It." Sometimes a nurse interprets this to mean that she must always "look for the best" in patients and disregard any negative feelings that may arise. This is unrealistic sentimentality. Another nurse may decide to "suspend judgment" about all her patients. To suspend open condemnation is commendable, but to put one's mind in neutral and pretend indifference to all that occurs is folly. By disregarding her own feelings, the nurse can make herself an "It." This "I–Thou" feeling works both ways.

A student nurse felt very sorry for a middle-aged woman who was one of her first patients. The patient seemed to be very sick. After a few days, however, the student noted that the patient had additional complaints whenever her husband failed to call, and when he did visit her, she spent the time describing her ills to him. The nurse began to think that the woman was childish and foolish. She wanted to shake the patient back into her senses. The student kept asking herself, "How can I show a loving Christian attitude when I have this inner disgust for the patient?"

This student must first recognize the negative elements in the patient's personality. She assumed an unrealistic attitude, for she believed all manner of good things about the patient at first. Later she accepted this mistaken evaluation as a part of her inexperience because she was learning. Finally, after she had examined her own hurt pride and healed it with humility, she was ready to understand why the patient resorted to this behavior.

Unrealistic sentimentality defeated this student. She did not see the patient as a person with some good and some bad qualities. Instead, she moved from pity to condemnation.

Another nurse sought to avoid this danger by refraining from any judgment. When an attractive woman about her size and height was assigned to her, she thought, "My, what a pretty woman." But when she read on the chart that the woman had septicemia due to a criminal abortion, she said to herself, "Goodness, she isn't as pretty as I thought." Then she tried to erase the thought and act naturally with the patient. But it isn't easy to be natural when one is on guard against a value judgment which is suppressed. The nurse tried to see this woman apart from her history. To pretend that the past was not there made for very superficial conversation. A deeper relationship would have developed if the nurse had thought, "I don't approve of this woman's conduct, but she is my patient. What can I mean to a person with this kind of background?" The nurse could then have accepted the woman as she was, rather than cut off a section of her personality that ought not to be. The move to what ought to be in personality depends first upon acknowledging what already is.

The need for a nurse to see both the patient and herself as a "Thou" may also be illustrated from the attitudes of some male patients toward nurses. One student nurse described an "I don't care" type of patient. He was a thirty-year-old man who did not seem to care if he was covered or not when a nurse came into his room. The student said that she hated to go into his room because he had no regard for her feelings. "He just seemed to think that I was a *thing*," she said. The student resented this attitude because she thought of herself as a "Thou," that is, a person in a profession, not as an "It" or an automaton in a uniform.

In another instance, a student nurse described a senile patient whom she pitied "because he was too weak to cover himself." The student was not shocked or indignant because she knew that the old man was physically weak and unaware of what he was doing.

On other occasions, when a patient is embarrassed by an enema, an irrigation, or a bath, the nurse may be so busy trying to make the patient physically comfortable and psychologically at ease that she forgets her own personal embarrassment.

In all these examples, a concern for persons—either the nurse or patient, is primary. A sick person's morality is not measured by the yard of well-draped bed linen.

Right or Wrong?

In this chapter we have considered the personal ethical standards which are basic to the Hebrew-Christian tradition. We have related these to issues which are common to nurses. For a discussion of other ethical decisions, I would suggest Howard Kee's *Making Ethical Decisions*[13] and *Christian Ethics* by Georgia Hankness.[14]

Nurses are also faced with specialized moral issues in their profession, such as are involved in abortion, sterilization, and euthanasia. Now that the general moral tone for ethical decisions has been presented, we will consider more unique problems of medical ethics in the next chapter.

---

[13] Philadelphia: Westminster Press, 1957.
[14] New York: Abingdon Press, 1957.

12. Specialized Problems in Nursing Ethics

Truthful Attitudes

ATTITUDES ARE AS IMPORTANT as deeds in Christian morality. A nurse's willingness to be truthful is as essential as the ensuing intellectual effort required to speak the truth. Both the desire and the method of communication are important, but the method will be conditioned by the motivations.

Therefore, as in the discussion of truthfulness in the chapter on death, the need for an attitude of honesty must be stressed. This means several things in the nurse's relation to any patient:

(1) A nurse is obliged to tell the truth as she sees it according to her best knowledge. By "best knowledge" is meant that she will be as accurate as she can within the limitations of her training and her ability.

(2) A nurse is obliged to tell the truth at all times. She may not distort reality to please other people or to make circumstances easy for herself. As Dr. Cabot asked in *The Meaning of Right and Wrong*, "How can we ever be sure where a conscientious liar will draw the line?"

(3) When a limitation is placed upon her ability to speak the truth, the nurse should still be honest. If a doctor has given strict orders for no one to discuss death or a diagnosis with a patient, a nurse should truthfully answer the patient's questions by referring the sick one to the doctor. If a nurse has received informa-

tion in confidence from someone, she has a right to tell an inquisitive questioner, "I'm sorry, but I cannot discuss that with you." An example of this is seen in obstetrics: When neighbors call the hospital to ask about the weight of a child born seven months after the parents' marriage, the nurse, suspecting the motives behind the inquiry, may reply, "I'm sorry, but we don't give out that information."

(4) A person's desire not to know the truth should be respected. When the nurse senses a secret fear, she may seek by her attitude and attentiveness to encourage the patient to release the tension by talking about it. But if a person evades conversation about his condition, the nurse should not force unpleasant realities upon him unless it is essential for his well-being. A patient had been told by his doctor that he had inoperable cancer. The physician described it as a "large lump in your abdomen." Later, when a nurse visited the patient and asked about his condition, the man replied, "Oh, I'm O.K. The doctor says I just have a lump in my abdomen. They'll not operate on it, so I'm going home." The nurse did not correct the patient, for she saw that the reality of his condition was more than he could absorb at that time.

(5) A truthful attitude is not the same as impulsive desire to blurt out some devastating fact. A doctor rather than a nurse has primary responsibility for informing patients of his diagnosis and prognosis. A nurse should be comfortable in the limits of her role and expect the doctor to be comfortable enough in his to take the initiative in speaking of these things to patients. Once he does, the nurse should interpret illness in the light of the first moral principle, a concern for the person. A nurse is *not* giving primary thought to the patient's welfare when she blurts out some distressing fact which causes her great anxiety.

Student Nurse A. had always feared cancer because this disease was most dreaded by her mother, to whom she was still closely attached. When she was assigned to a patient who was to be operated on for cancer of the cervix, Miss A. was tense with anticipation of all the horrors she knew years ago at home. The evening before surgery the surgeon came in to describe the patient's condition and reassure her concerning the forthcoming operation. After the surgeon left, the patient said to Miss A., "Well, I just know it is better to have this thing removed—it's cancer, you know." Miss A. replied, "Oh, don't you worry—over 50 per cent of the patients who have cancer don't die, you know!"

Some preliminary orientation by the instructor and an exploration of the student's attitudes toward cancer might have saved both the nurse and the patient from such a scene as this. Miss A's. "knowledge" made her so anxious that she had to blurt it out.

Planned Parenthood

Nurses face the issue of planned parenthood, not only in their own lives when married, but also in general medical practice and in the five hundred or more birth-control and child-spacing clinics in the United States.

Joseph Fletcher writes in *Morals and Medicine* that moral control by men over their circumstances is an indispensable part of personal integrity.[1] The spacing of children and the control of conception is a moral issue because God has given men and women knowledge by which they may increase the health and well-being of their families.

An increase in knowledge may also increase moral responsibility. This is true of planned parenthood. Catholic and Protestant moralists are agreed that responsibility for the health and well-being of the entire future family is the mature motive necessary for the moral justification of child-spacing.[2] Father Kenny would permit periodic abstinence according to the rhythm method to prevent conception under one of the following conditions: When the physical and mental health of the mother would be endangered, from a medical point of view, by pregnancy; a deformed or retarded child is likely; there is financial inability to support a child; or there are cramped living quarters.[3] To these a fifth could be added: when there is a temporary stress situation which

---

[1] Princeton: Princeton University Press, 1954, p. 66.

[2] John P. Kenny, *Principles of Medical Ethics* (Westminster, Md.: Newman Press, 1952) pp. 94–95; Fletcher, *op. cit.*, pp. 75–88.

[3] *Ibid.*

will be relieved at a definite date in the near future, so that both husband and wife may give mature attention to each other and to their child.[4]

So far as motivation is concerned, most moralists are in agreement about birth control. The problem which separates Catholic and Protestant moralists has arisen out of increased knowledge of fertilization. In 1784 Father Spallanzani traced the movement of sperm. For a hundred years after this the method of birth control was not a burning issue. But in the past fifty years more positive opinions have been formulated by the Roman Catholic Church as well as the Protestant faiths. In 1925 the American Medical Association Committee on Obstetrics, Gynecology, and Abdominal Surgery endorsed birth control by contraceptive devices. In 1930 the Anglican bishops approved birth control, and the Federal Council of Churches in America soon made a like proclamation. At the same time, Catholics have become very active in legislation and in moral pronouncements against contraception. Father Kenny denounces it as immoral and places it in the same category with masturbation and prostitution.[5] He also maintains that "artificial preventative methods are injurious to the woman. . . . The habitual use of contraceptive devices can be a cause of sterility." [6] Only one medical authority for this opinion is cited.

Protestants and Jews should notice that Roman Catholic writers usually use strong language because they must overcome the passive opposition of many persons in the Roman Catholic Church in addition to the opinion and the practices of Protestants, Jews, and pagans. An Elmo Roper poll in 1943 indicated that a majority (54.9 per cent) of Catholic women in Connecticut favored birth control guidance, even though Connecticut is one of the two states which forbids such information by law. According to this poll, 84.9 per cent of all women aged 20–35 are in favor of marital contraception.

Protestant theologians believe that man is to use the knowledge given him by God to control nature and that this includes knowl-

---

[4] Agreement with Father Kenny's *reasons* does not mean that Protestants endorse the rhythm method.

[5] Kenny, *op. cit.*, p. 88.

[6] *Ibid.*, p. 86.

edge of contraceptive devices. Catholics assert that contraceptives are "unnatural" and "against nature." Although Protestants do not accept this, it makes sense to Catholic moralists because they believe that morality is based upon the use of reason in the interpretation of physical laws of nature, which are called the "natural laws." By defining the "unsafe period" of the rhythm cycle as a period in which nature intends fertility, it is argued that contraception during that period is "unnatural."

Some Catholics as well as Protestants use the story of Onan in Genesis 38:6–10 to condemn contraception and masturbation. Actually, Onan was condemned for irresponsibility. He would not fulfil the Mosaic law, which commanded that a man should continue the line for his deceased brother through the brother's wife who now became his wife. The emphasis was upon mature responsibility rather than upon prohibition of actions which are not even mentioned in the Bible.

From the Protestant point of view, sexual union between a husband and his wife should be an expression of love. It is more than a physical act only for the purpose of procreation.

Permanent Prevention of Pregnancy

A mature morality obligates the individual to consider both the present and the future welfare of each individual. Impulsive, thoughtless acts today may bring grief to the doer of the act as well as to others. Therefore, within the bounds of human knowledge, the individual is responsible for consistent planning for the future well-being of the family and the race.

Advances in the predictive skills of medicine have raised new moral problems. One of these is sterilization. On one hand, the early detection of certain diseases may cause a physician to warn a wife that pregnancy will, in the light of present medical knowledge, aggravate her condition to such serious proportions that she could not function as a mother or perhaps would die while she was with child. On the other hand, other medical discoveries may cause a physician to encourage another wife to become pregnant in the face of known malfunctions or diseases which might have killed her before the advent of these new discoveries.

In addition to the need to make decisions about the life and health of the prospective mother, the issue of health for the unborn child must also be considered. If the wife suffers from a hereditary disease, malformation, or malfunction which would permanently injure the child either in the womb or at birth, on the basis of accumulated medical evidence the physician will probably warn her against pregnancy.

If the risks of pregnancy are so grave that the death or permanent disability of mother or child would follow, some physicians advise permanent prevention of pregnancy through sterilization. Most Protestant pastors would support the physician in this decision if he had taken the precaution, necessary in many states, of bringing in a consultant to confirm this serious recommendation. Reasons for this stand are as follows:

(1) God has made husband and wife "one flesh." This union is a sacred bond which should not be jeopardized by the wife's becoming pregnant against the advice of competent medical authorities. Sterilization is morally justifiable to prevent an impaired union through the crippling of the mother or the child, the death of the child, deep guilt in both parents, or a complete rupture of the union through the death of the mother. Here is an example:

Mrs. A. was the mother of a baby boy of whom she was very proud. The problem was that Mrs. A. had a condition in which "discolored wart-like" projections, known as neurofibromas, appeared all over her body.

The nurse was giving care when the doctor made his morning visit. He talked with the patient and told her that her surgery was scheduled for the next morning. After the doctor left, the patient seemed slightly worried.

PATIENT: What does the doctor do when he ties the tubes? I mean, is it going to be hard on me?

NURSE: Of course, you might have some discomfort from the operation and stitches, but most patients want to get up in a day or two.

PATIENT: I really did not want to have this done. This is only my third baby and I wanted five or six.

NURSE: Boys or girls?

PATIENT: I have an all-male family now. (*pause*) You know, I never thought of that. Dr. E. told me that my condition is thought to be inherited, and it gets worse with every pregnancy. So, since I haven't any girls, they can't have this condition.

NURSE: That's something to think about. And now your decision will not seem so hard.

PATIENT: Really, I'm very proud of my boys, and I'll just be "queen of the house." (*She laughed here, was in a much better mood, and seemingly not worried any more.*)

(2) Sexual union is a God-given right to all couples who become "one flesh." It should not be impaired by the fear that some accident or miscalculation during marital relations may do irreparable harm to the wife or the prospective child. Parenthood is a responsible decision which is to be guided by concern for all persons, present and future, in the family. It is unjust to ask a couple to weigh the God-given renewal of personality and their expression of love through intercourse against the possible death of the wife and an unborn child. Therefore, when the overwhelming weight of medical opinion favors sterilization, it should be chosen both for the physical and the emotional and spiritual health of both parents.

On the other hand, there are grave warnings which must be issued against irresponsible or premature sterilization. Usually the permanent prevention of pregnancy involves married women. At times a mother will seek sterilization even though there is no physical danger involved in future pregnancy. In such cases the physician is morally justified in advising contraceptive devices or techniques and dissuading the woman from permanent prevention of pregnancy. No one knows all circumstances of the future. Even if the woman believes she has enough children now and the budget or the nerves can stand no more, circumstances and conditions may change for her. The husband may die, and she may remarry. She would probably desire children of this second marriage.

Roman Catholic parents receive an additional warning from their church against sterilization. It is not to be a direct action. It may only be indirect. For example, a Catholic physician may not sterilize a patient because of the dangers of pregnancy because of a heart ailment, tuberculosis, or a scarred and weakened uterus. But he may indirectly cause sterilization by removing a pathological uterus or by irradiating ovaries because of carcinoma. In Roman Catholic moral theology, the "law of double effect" teaches that if the physician's intention is to safeguard the health of the patient and the sterilization is an indirect result of his good intentions, it is permissible.[7]

When Roman Catholic patients avoid their priest because they allow sterilization, some of them are still confused. It is difficult enough to decide that the permanent prevention is necessary; it is even harder when powerful religious prohibitions are being violated. The nurse has a responsibility to show the utmost concern for such patients without agreeing or disagreeing with their decision:

A twenty-six-year-old mother was scheduled for sterilization several days after the birth of her sixth child. She was very tired on the morning of the operation. About noon, when she was being readied for the operation, she began asking the nurse questions about her trip to surgery.

PATIENT: I tried my best to get out of this operation.

NURSE: Oh?

PATIENT: Yes—and I wish there was time to back out now. But I guess I can't. There is just so much involved.

NURSE: Yes—it is a very hard decision for anyone to make.

PATIENT: Well, I keep thinking—what if all my children were to get killed in a car wreck or something and I'd want to have some more? But, even if I did, the same thing might happen as before—my blood pressure gets higher and my health worse with each pregnancy. And we're Catholic, and that makes it even harder to decide.

NURSE: I'm sure you and your husband considered all these things before you made any definite decision.

PATIENT: Yes. As a matter of fact, we've been discussing it ever since I was three months pregnant. My husband just doesn't want me to have any more kids. For one thing, we just can't afford to support any more. (*She began to sound more calm and more confident of her decision.*) And my doctor assured me this operation was

---

[7] *Ibid.*, pp. 172–74.

the best thing for my health. So the only thing for me to do is to go ahead with it.

NURSE: Well, since you considered everything involved so carefully before deciding, I admire you for sticking to your decision now.

At that time, another nurse came in to give the patient her preoperative medication. We encouraged her to relax and left her alone.

The patient was concerned because this was preventative sterilization. If it had been curative, that is, an indirect result of procedures which would alleviate disease, she would have felt that it would be accepted by her church.

Religious beliefs and medical knowledge are the components of a mature decision about sterilization.

The Termination of Pregnancy

There are reasons for caution about the termination of pregnancy. In the first place, advances in the healing arts enable many women to survive and deliver healthy infants despite certain malformations and diseases which made delivery fatal to women in past generations. Second, a mature morality demands that people take responsibility for decisions, even if future circumstances cause inconvenience. In a previous chapter the incident was related about the death of a young man whose wife was with child. As a mature person, she was expected to bear her sorrow with the help of God and the Christian community. Grievous as was the loss of her husband, the loss did not in itself justify an abortion.

Within this interrelationship of morality and medicine there are questions which arise around two terms, "responsibility" and "personality." When a man and woman cohabit on a basis of mutual consent, they are responsible for the natural results of their action whether they intend to assume it or not. An immature couple may not desire children, but if conception occurs, it may not be terminated because their social life would be "inconvenienced." They will have to do something about the immaturity within themselves. In contrast, an older couple whose children are grown are not justified in asking for an abortion even though the woman thought she could no longer conceive, although both of them believe that they have already fulfilled all of their duties in regard to rearing children.

Responsibility also continues upon a couple who may have intended to have children but who change their minds as they begin to realize the multiple adjustments of parenthood. They accepted the challenge of parenthood when the wife became pregnant. Their first decision may not be reversed.

Emotional exhaustion may be accepted by some as a reason to relieve a woman of responsibility for pregnancy, but it does not. It is believed that a majority of abortions are performed upon married women, often women with several children. They use as justification the reasons that they are "worn out" and incapable of "standing up to another one." The answer to this problem is not to be sought in the termination of pregnancy but in a thorough investigation of the husband-wife relationship.

The mother of four children was visited by a pastor and a Sunday school teacher who wished to enrol the family in Sunday school. The mother could scarcely hold back tears, for this was the first visit from anyone since her family moved to this city. As she recovered herself, she began to speak with desperate hope of the possibility that for an hour during Sunday school she could relax away from the children. She looked sad as she said, "But I don't know if my husband would take me or not." When the pastor asked why, the mother told how she assumed all responsibility for the children and the home. "In fact," she said, "he won't even help with the baby—and another's on the way. I don't know how I'll manage, but he says that if I get pregnant it's my fault." She had always feared to ask her husband about contraceptives.

The teacher encouraged the woman by saying that she would arrange transportation and ask some men in the church to call on her husband.

A month later the mother asked the pastor to call again. During the several pastoral visits which followed, she told how she had always feared to ask anything of her husband. Now she wanted him to take some responsibility but didn't know how to go about it. With the pastor's counsel, she began to think better of herself. She developed enough courage to tell her husband to discipline the oldest boy "because he's your son and he needs a man's guidance." The husband, who was always very vain about his "manhood," responded well to this and was doubly pleased when he found that his son enjoyed his company.

After five pastoral interviews, the mother told her husband, "I want you to see how I change a diaper on Susan, because she'll need you when the little one comes. I'll be busy with the baby for a while, so you'll have to manage one at night while I take care of the other." The husband started to reply negatively but then remembered that a recent visitor from the men's Sunday school class had talked about changing diapers on his own children. The husband respected the visitor, who was a lawyer in the same office building with him. So, to try out this new concept of fatherhood, he said, "O.K., I'll watch."

Several months after the child was born, the husband, holding her in his arms, said with ill-concealed pride to one of his friends, "Well *I* didn't change a diaper until this kid came along, but I'm quite an expert now."

The life of the entire family was more abundant because the mother helped the husband assume a father's responsibility. Instead of using the retreat of abortion, they learned to face life on a shared basis.

On some occasions termination of pregnancy may be desired because the child is conceived out of wedlock. The help of a pastor and social workers should be sought on such occasions, since the couple will need guidance. Unfortunately, only the woman is readily accessible to medical and other help. The complex issues which enter into the unmarried mother's desire for a child and the sociological and psychological resources for help are described in *Out of Wedlock* by Leontine Young [8] and "Understanding the Psychology of the Unmarried Mother," published by the Family Service Association, 192 Lexington Avenue, New York 16, New York.

Both the unwed mother and the nurse have a moral obligation

---

[8] New York: McGraw-Hill, 1954.

in such situations. The mother is as morally responsible to bear the child as she is psychologically responsible for the conception. At times the mother may verbally admit this, but more often it may seem like a disturbing dream rather than the real reason for her present condition. A teen-age girl, the afternoon after she had returned from the delivery room, said to a student nurse:

PATIENT: I miss my church life very much. I worked in the nursery at our church, and that's where my real love is. See what my love of children got me into? (*She points to her abdomen.*)
NURSE: Are you sure it was your love for children that caused your condition?
PATIENT: You think I'm sorry, don't you? Well, I'm not sorry I did it, just sorry I got caught. Do you have a boy friend?
NURSE: Yes, I do.
PATIENT: Are you engaged?
NURSE: No, I'm not. I hope to be some day.
PATIENT: Me, too. I want to get married and have a house load of kids.

The nurse's question about love for children indicated her feeling that this patient was merely promiscuous and didn't really want a child. She followed it up later with another statement to the patient: "We never know the right things to do until we've done them wrong once. I hope you've learned that lesson now."

Unfortunately, the nurse gave the patient the wrong advice. At the same time, the nurse's natural urge to warn and admonish was not formulated in a way which the patient could accept. The nurse regarded the patient as a different kind of human being. She did not see the patient as someone who might really want to have a child because the patient had chosen a morally unacceptable method of achieving her conscious or unconscious goal.

The nurse's responsibility is to accept the unwed mother as a "Thou," another woman whose desire for a child has been mixed with feelings of love and hate against parents. The nurse is not to suspend judgment but to know how to judge aright that she may lead the mother to accept help.

There is one unfortunate situation in which a woman has no moral responsibility for her pregnancy: namely, when rape results in conception. If a woman is grabbed from her husband on the streets of New York by four men whom she has never seen before, driven to a secluded spot, and sexually assaulted, that is rape. If a student nurse attends a fraternity party where there are no chaperons, drinks with her date, and goes with him to one of the upstairs bedrooms where they do some heavy petting, the result is not rape, even though she may scream when she realizes that both of them are too intoxicated to stop the consummation of their sexual desires. In the former instance the woman was not morally responsible; in the latter she was as responsible as her partner.

It is at this point that Catholic and Protestant moralists have divergent opinions. No matter what the conditions that result in rape are, a Catholic patient must not allow the termination of pregnancy. Father Kenny states that when a woman has been raped, she may receive a douche within three hours. After that time, nothing is permissible, since any douche after fertilization is murder of an innocent child even though the father is guilty.[9] Father Edwin Healy would allow a douche within sixteen hours.[10]

Personality is another key term in a discussion of abortion. Since the term "personality" is not used in the Bible and has undergone tremendous modification throughout the centuries, it is a many-faceted word whose meaning is related to and determined by many philosophical, theological, and psychological factors.

In *Personality and Religion*[11] Paul Johnson states that personality combines individuality and companionship. Both a sense of separateness and a sense of togetherness are essential in a person. Wayne Oates lists the common factors in psychological and theological explanations of personality in *The Religious Dimensions of Personality*.[12] Both of these authorities examine "personality" as a term which is like a jewel that gives off a different hue

---

[9] Kenny, *op. cit.*, pp. 89–90.
[10] *Medical Ethics* (Chicago: Loyola University Press, 1956), p. 277.
[11] New York: Abingdon Press, 1957.
[12] New York: Association Press, 1957.

with each new reflection of a facet. They do not attempt to define minute details concerning personality, such as the exact time when a fetus becomes a person.

Not many Protestants are disturbed by this lack of psychological and physiological evidence concerning the advent of personality because they believe that the salvation of a person is not dependent upon the act of baptism.[13] But Roman Catholics do believe that the baptism of a soul is necessary for its salvation. The time when a fetus becoms a "soul" is therefore of great importance to them. By accepting the theory that the "soul" appears at conception, the Roman Catholic Church requires that a fetus be treated as a person.[14] One application of this theory is seen in the Catholic teaching concerning abortion. Father Healy states that the death of the mother, and perhaps of the child also, is merely a physical evil; but a therapeutic abortion would be direct killing of an innocent human being (the fetus), and this is a moral evil. Therefore, the physical evil is the lesser of the two evils.[15]

Although there are few times when such a choice must be made, Protestants are opposed to the death of a mother under such circumstances for the following reasons: (1) The husband-wife union, created by God, is not to be torn asunder through the wife's death as the result of adherence to the theories of men. (2) The wife may be able to bear and nurse a normal child in the future. Her future potential as a mother should not be sacrificed because of a present emergency which may be therapeutically remedied. (3) Neither psychology nor physiology provide any conclusive evidence as to the time when an embryo becomes a person. (4) Salvation is a spiritual gift of God, not a ritual dispensed by men. The importance of a sacrament is given different significance by denominations, theologians, the college of cardinals, and the period of history.

The preceding remarks are used to illustrate differences concerning the meaning of personality. They do not mean that

---

[13] Methodist, Baptist, and Presbyterian, for example. More concern about baptism is expressed by Lutheran, Episcopal, and Churches of Christ.

[14] Kenny, *op. cit.*, pp. 131–38; Healy, *op. cit.*, pp. 358 ff.

[15] *Ibid.*, p. 196.

Catholics prefer to kill mothers. Rev. Gerald Kelly clarifies this by writing: "It should be clear that any direct (i.e., the intentional) taking of innocent life is never permissible. Any procedure which would result in death for either the mother or the child (or for any other innocent person) can be justified only when the death is an unintended and unavoidable by-product of the procedure." [16]

Since a discussion of the beginnings of personality involves many other moral problems, such as God's love and hereditary defects, it is recommended that nurses read two chapters in *Religious Dimensions of Personality* [17] by Wayne Oates: "The Religious Dimensions of Man's Heredity," and "Religious Dimensions of Man's Birth."

As with many of life's problems, it is not possible to give answers for every situation in one book. Answers are difficult enough even when many of the facts and feelings are known, for human beings are so varied, and moral principles have a way of conflicting at the very time when people yearn most for the absolute solution. A recent fictional example of this is seen in the thoughts of Dr. Swain and Nurse Kelly concerning the pregnancy of Selena Cross.[18]

The Birth Process

It may be said that this detailed examination of moral issues is not intended to be a final, legal decision. Morality and medicine are disciplines in which the case as it *is* must be related to what *ought* to be. Situations are too fluid and changing for exacting, unalterable pronouncements. For example, in addition to vehement medical opposition to anesthesia in childbirth a hundred years ago, there was the opposition of those who believed that woman's existence is justified only through the suffering of childbirth.

Throughout this chapter, therefore, an attempt is being made

---

[16] *Medico-Moral Problems* (St. Louis: Catholic Hospital Association, 1957), p. 65.

[17] New York: Association Press, 1947.

[18] Grace Metalious, *Peyton Place* (New York: Dell Publishing Co., 1956), pp. 199–205, 213–27.

to present general ethical principles and to illustrate them with contemporary conversations between patients and professional people. The great emphasis is upon persons as God's creation rather than upon man-made religious legalism. The theme is the "I–Thou" relationship.

This theme, recurrent in our discussion of conception and pregnancy, appears also in the birth of a child.

Nurse N. assisted Dr. C. in the delivery of a child whose skull was distended with fluid. "Hydrocephalic—hopeless," murmured the doctor as he performed a craniotomy. The nurse knew that the parents had not given their consent to this procedure, nor did they know that anything was wrong with the fetus. The doctor reported to them that the child was a hopelessly deformed one who died at birth.

The nurse was incensed by this, yet she was torn by uncertainty. The child *probably* would have died anyway, or would have been totally helpless. Or would he? Was the craniotomy justified?

The procedure was not justified unless the life of the mother was in such danger that it was medically necessary to save her. In God's sight, any life is sacred because he created man in his image, and his Son died for everyone. Because human life is not man's creation and because God paid the greatest price to perfect it, individuals have no right to decide that an "imperfect" life should be destroyed. The child is not an "It," a distended skull; he is a "Thou," one for whom Christ died.

A hydrocephalic child lived for two days after birth. At the announcement of death, the father was torn between grief and relief. The mother cried for a while, and when her husband went downstairs, she said, "I know why it is. It is God's punishment for the way we have lived. Do you think God punishes us?"

The student nurse replied, "I don't think that God punishes us by taking away our children. What you have suffered raises many questions, I know, and often you need someone to talk with who is skilled and understanding, like our chaplain. I hope that when he calls you will talk with him about the question that you raised with me."

The concept of God who has revealed himself as a "Thou" determined the answer which the student could give.

Mrs. M. had three children, all of which were girls. Mrs. M.'s fourth child was born only one hour after her arrival in the labor unit. In this short length of time she talked constantly of how much she wanted a boy. When Mrs. M. awakened in the hospital recovery room, the nurse told her, as is the custom, that she was now the mother of a lovely baby girl. Mrs. M. didn't seem to think the baby so lovely, because she cried. This didn't seem so strange, since she was still under the effect of the anesthetic.

A student nurse took Mrs. M. to her room and asked her if she was ready to see her little girl as they passed the nursery. Mrs. M. quickly said, "No, it's a girl. I don't want to see that little girl. I wanted a boy. Why couldn't I have a little boy!"

By this time Mrs. M. had fully recovered from the anesthetic, and the statement took the nurse by surprise. Her first thought was that something must be wrong with the patient. In answer to her question, the nurse told her that there were many things in God's will and plan for us that we cannot understand, but that he had sent her this little girl for her to love and care for, and he must have thought it would be best for her to have a little girl this time. Also, possibly the next time she could have a boy. The patient smiled as the nurse left the room.

The mother, for various reasons which are not explored in this interview, saw the infant as an "It," a girl. The student nurse helped her to see her as a "Thou," a little person dependent on a mother's love.

The Baptism of Children

If a child is dying, baptism becomes an issue for Roman Catholic, Eastern Orthodox, Lutheran, Evangelical and Reformed, and Episcopal parents as well as those of some other denominations. Roman Catholic moralists prescribe immediate measures to provide baptism for a fetus, for they believe that an unbaptised baby, although it will live in great natural happiness, will never see God.[19] Some Catholic moralists feel so strongly about this that they advise Catholic nurses to baptize secretly every dying child even if the parents oppose it.[20] If a priest cannot come in time, any person may perform an emergency baptism who has reached the

---

[19] Healy, *op. cit.*, p. 358.

[20] *Ibid.*, p. 367.

age of reason and "who is both able and willing to carry out the intention of the church." [21] Even enemies of the church and those without faith may baptize. However, the person performing the baptism must perform it according to the intention of the Roman Catholic Church or the baptism will not be valid. Father Healy states, therefore,

> It must of course be recognized that some persons simply cannot see the existence of such an obligation and that others not only deny its existence but would consider themselves guilty of moral fault were they to act according to this teaching. As we have mentioned above, each individual must follow the promptings of his own conscience. If his conscience tells him that so to act would be morally wrong, he should of course avoid that course of action. Hence those who are convinced that baptizing a dying infant would be illicit would be guilty of no moral fault in refraining from this act.[22]

Father Healy then adds that the action would certainly please the parents and near relatives of the infant who see in baptism an inestimable blessing.

It is primarily the doctor's responsibility to inform the parents that their child is in danger, unless someone else in the hospital such as a nursing supervisor or a chaplain takes the initiative. When the doctor or nurse has done this, they may ask the parents if they wish a clergyman to be called. Usually there is time for the priest or minister to come and baptize the infant. In *extreme* cases, when no priest or minister is available, Catholic and some Protestant nurses take the further responsibility of pouring water on the infant's head until some runs off the forehead while saying, "I baptize thee in the name of the Father and of the Son and of the Holy Ghost. Amen." They should then sign a statement indicating when and where this rite took place.

Other nurses may or may not assume responsibility for this rite. If conscience prompts a nurse to do so, the baptism is valid. If her religious teachings cry out against it, the nurse should not because she would be both compromising her faith and invalidating the rite. If she does not believe in salvation through the

---

[21] *Ibid.*, p. 168.

[22] *Ibid.*, pp. 358–59.

baptism of infants, her intentions are not those of the Roman Catholic Church, and Roman Catholic moralists would declare the baptism invalid.[23]

It is well, therefore, to know the religious affiliation of all personnel in the delivery room or obstetrical wing, so that a person who accepts the intention of the Roman Catholic Church may be called to administer emergency baptism for infants. In addition, hospitals might have a form on baptism giving the name of the infant, the date, and by whom he was baptized.

Detailed information on Catholic directives may be obtained from a pamphlet issued by the Catholic Hospital Association, 1438 S. Grand Blvd., St. Louis 4, Missouri.

The Right to Die

In nursing and medical ethics there are at least three problems connected with the right to die: the prolongation of existence, euthanasia, and suicide.

When are nurses and doctors prolonging life, and when are they prolonging the act of dying? Medical personnel face three pressures as they seek to make a decision. There is the emotional reaction of the family, the attitude of the patient, and the professional drive of the nurse and doctor. All three of these may or may not be present in any one instance. The second, the patient's attitude, will be discussed under euthanasia.

The first influence may be that of the family. Sometimes members of a family may have strong feelings of guilt concerning their treatment of the patient and may wish extraordinary means to be used for his comfort or recovery. When it becomes obvious that the family insists on more plasma or drugs than the physician deems necessary, the nurse should alert the chaplain, ask the family if they have called their pastor in this time of distress, and reassure them that all that can be done is being done.

Other families have to make difficult financial decisions. Oxygen tents, intravenous fluids, blood transfusions, antibiotics, blood substitutes, and such are an enormous drain upon family

---

[23] *Ibid.*, p. 359.

resources even if they have group health insurance. If the family discusses this problem with the nurse, she should first seek to know how well they understand the doctor's advice and then suggest that there is a difference between essential and extraordinary measures for prolonging life. Rest, bedside care, food, and medication may be all that the physician has prescribed. These are essential measures which any family should accept. But exceptional, expensive supportive measures which are not judged essential by the doctor should not be sought by the family. There is a moral obligation to the living as well as to the dying. Sometimes the patient knows this and implores the family not to use up meager savings or go disastrously into debt when there is no hope for recovery.

The inner pressure of a professional person must also be evaluated. The urge to succeed, to wrest victory from certain defeat, or to be the first triumphant user of some new supportive measure may press upon some doctors and nurses. There are also the personal ties to certain patients which urge doctors and nurses to exhaust every means, indicated or beyond the realm of probability, to sustain the life of this person. When the nurse recognizes her personal involvement, she may attempt to control it. One graduate nurse spent her off-duty hours at the bedside of a terminally ill patient. The necessary nursing care was already adequate, but she wanted to do something special "because when I was a child, he was like a father to me." She knew what her actions meant and found fulfilment in them.

On the other hand, a staff member may defend unnecessary measures without regard for the family. An elderly man had been comatose in the hospital for two weeks. At the end of the first week, the family physician told the patient's wife that there was little left to do but make her husband as comfortable as possible during the few days which were left to him. The wife accepted the situation. The physician then went on vacation, and a resident took charge of the case. He immediately ordered several new and expensive drugs and informed the wife that she should not be such a fatalist about her husband. Two days later the wife said to a nurse, "Oh, what can I do! I can't pay for all this; I've asked all I can from my son. And look at him—he just lies there, with all those sores on him, heaving all over when he breathes. I just can't stand it!"

The nurse replied curtly, "Mrs. Jackson, Dr. Boon is one of the best doctors on our staff. We are fortunate to obtain his services since your doctor is away. You should be grateful for these new drugs. They may save Mr. Jackson's life." Three days later Mr. Jackson died. Mrs. Jackson was completely drained, financially, emotionally—even spiritually. For after her conversation with the nurse, the latter had contacted the chaplain, who had taken Mrs. Jackson into the chapel and questioned her motives in what she said to the nurse. He implied that she should be ashamed of herself for desiring her husband's death. She should have faith, he said, pray to God, and pay the pharmacy without complaint.

Euthanasia, "easy death," sanctions the painless termination of life for those suffering from incurable and extremely painful diseases. The discussion usually proceeds into other areas such as the elimination of idiots, senile and "hopelessly insane" persons, and habitual criminals.

Proponents of euthanasia usually argue for what is most desirable to the individual and to the society in which he lives, and man and his social world become the measure of judgment. This argument disregards the responsibility of man to his Creator. Christianity teaches that this life is a preparation for a better life through the inheritance of eternal life. Men are to surrender themselves to God's authority. To kill a person on the basis of a personal judgment concerning such an elusive and mysterious phenomenon as suffering is to take authority which is not the prerogative of men.

This same principle of submission to the Creator also applies to suicide. Man's life is not his own, because in Christian belief man has been bought with the price of God's own Son. In addition, nearly all people believe that God is the Creator of human life and that he alone has authority to terminate it.

The problems surrounding the fact of suicide have three moral implications: each person should exercise care in the handling of his own life; each person should exercise care in the treatment of others; each person's reaction to suicide should begin with this question: "What effect will my expressions have upon the bereaved family and upon all who hear?"

These are general rather than specific criteria because the act of suicide may have its origin in any of many causes. The deeper, underlying causes may or may not be recognized. On occasion there are no readily discernible clues, and the act may seem to erupt from the unfathomable depths of personality. At other times the causes may be more demonstrable, and prevention may be more effective. It may be a dependent person's reaction to a broken love affair, a psychotic attempt to solve an unconscious problem, or the reaction of a sensitive person to the despair of the society in which he lives.

When relatives who have been called come to the emergency room, they may feel grief, guilt, or hatred. If the nurse can react to these mourners as she would to any bereaved family, this attitude may give them help to handle their emotions. They can at least give vent to feelings of grief. To meet them in stifled horror is to cut them off from human communication at a time when they are desperately seeking companionship and understanding.

Sometimes the relatives have questions about why. No one knows the full explanation, and any attempt may make matters worse. One sister of a brother who committed suicide said to her pastor, "If you'd had to listen to all the reasons and explanations I've listened to, you'd want to bite nails in two!" An honest, "I'm sorry, but we don't know," is safe.

The question "Is he saved?" can be answered only by God. If a person has had faith in God, he is God's child no matter how sick, depressed, or bitter he may become. Although some persons condemn the person who commits suicide, they are taking God's judgment into their own hands. Protestants and Catholics condemn suicide but not the individual, since his judgment was probably impaired by mental illness.

Nurses also minister to persons who have attempted suicide. These patients need the attention of both a minister and a doctor. If they are on medical or surgical wards, as they gradually emerge from a state of depression they may become disturbed by feelings of guilt. They need acceptance without being subjected to superficial reassurance. On the third day after she had attempted to kill herself, a young mother began talking about it to her nurse.

NURSE: I see you have pictures of your children on the dresser.

PATIENT: Yes, one four, one two, and one three months. Poor things, they've all had colds this winter, one after another. My husband was away so much, and I had to stay up and nurse them. It just got me down, I guess.

NURSE: Yes, it can.

PATIENT: I mean, well, not so much the colds—but not having any friends in a new city, you know. We were all alone. I was used to family and folks dropping in. Oh, I don't know—

NURSE: Moving can be difficult.

PATIENT: But how could a person get into a state of mind like I did? My pastor came by last night, and he said that it was not a sin to be weak and run down from sickness. But I never thought I'd do a thing like that.

NURSE: So your pastor feels that God understands and forgives?

PATIENT: Yes, that's what he said.

The nurse showed her acceptance of the patient by reflecting the patient's feeling about sickness and loneliness. She did not attempt to move beyond the pastor, who probably led the woman to talk about the things which she recalled with the nurse. Instead, she reinforced the pastor's attempt to show this patient that weakness of itself is not sin. The patient was probably too much a perfectionist to accept this at once. The nurse did not begin an argument with the patient. Instead, she ended the conversation by asking if the minister was to call again.

Persons who attempt suicide may be admitted to the psychiatric section of a hospital. When a person is so emotionally disturbed that he is dominated by unconscious impulses, it is most difficult to fix blame for his actions. Questions like these lead into the area of religion and psychiatry that will be considered in the next chapter.

13. Religion and Psychiatry

CHRISTIANITY FINDS PRACTICAL EXPRESSION in the nurse's understanding of, and her relationship with, psychiatric patients. Gwen Tudor studied the ability of nurses to maintain relationship with mental hospital patients who sought to withdraw from all human contacts. The investigator found that some patients were so successful in their use of annoying or repulsive mannerisms that the staff began to ignore these patients without being aware of what had occurred. However, as a result of the investigator's interest, one student nurse developed some response from a very withdrawn patient. It was not an easy relationship. When the student nurse made such simple requests as "Do you want pineapple or tomato juice?" the patient would begin to scream. But the student stayed with the patient. Because she did stay, the patient began to handle her disturbances in a more successful manner. There was less striking out and kicking.

In time the student was able to move the patient toward group participation on the ward. The patient began to regain hope in her own recovery because one person had evidenced enthusiasm for her as a person.[1] Whether the student was consciously aware of the religious significance of her attitudes or not, she had fulfilled the Christian ethic in her personal concern for an unnoticed and withdrawn person.

[1] "A Sociopsychiatric Nursing Approach to Intervention in a Problem of Mutual Withdrawal on a Mental Hospital Ward," *Psychiatry*, XV (May, 1952), 193–217.

The nurse's philosophy of life, her inner source of spiritual renewal in the face of hopelessness and despair, and her basic faith in persons as God's creation are essential factors in her psychiatric nursing.

Religion is also important in nursing as a form of communication. The intangible Christian attitudes of faith such as patience and love have been discussed in earlier chapters. The use of religious language in the psychoses must also be considered. In *The Exploration of the Inner World* [2] Anton Boisen examined the content of thought found in 173 mental hospital patients. He found that many patients were filled with a sense of the mysterious. They spoke of dark and forbidding images which came into their conscious minds. Sometimes they used religious language to describe these thoughts.

Many of these patients also had a sense of peril. They were like the patient seen by a student nurse on her first day in the psychiatric section of a large hospital. This woman clutched the student's arm and told her a vision had revealed to her that the families of all her friends were to be destroyed by a hurricane. The patient regretted that although she had told her friends to repent, they had not done so. Now she must lead the nurses and doctors to repentance, lest they suffer a great catastrophe as well.

Other patients may feel a great sense of personal responsibility. Their ideation is revealed in conversations like the following:

PATIENT: The light has gone out of my family's life.

NURSE: Why do you say that?

PATIENT: Because I'm here in the hospital and can't be at home to help my family lay by the corn! I have to take all the responsibility for what goes on at home. My father can't do it by himself. I don't know what my married sisters will do without me to protect them. How will all those children get along in school? I used to ride by on my bicycle every day and wave to them. I've just got to get out of the hospital so that I can go back and do my work. The whole world is in darkness.

Some patients use religious language to express an erotic involvement. One patient explained to a nurse that she was the

---

[2] New York: Harper & Brothers, 1936.

Virgin Mary. At times God would "take her." She believed that she was now impregnated by God and would conceive Jesus. When the student nurse asked the ward physician about this, he commented that the patient had a very close attachment to her father. She had never married because she needed to stay home and take care of him after her mother had died. The patient could not express her strong emotional desire for her father but could describe it symbolically in religious terms. God represented her father.

Religious Language and Attitudes

Both the religious attitudes of the nurse and the religious communications of the patient are important in psychiatric nursing. When the nurse deals with highly disturbed people, she must consider how her religious ministry will be interpreted. Her religious conversation with patients must be carefully evaluated. The most common error of students who have meager supervision in the relationship between religion and nursing is to forget the religious restrictions which are imposed on a psychiatric unit. This does not refer to the warnings of some nursing instructors or doctors to shun discussions about religion. Instead, it has to do with the unexamined assumptions of some nurses that they can talk about religion with psychiatric patients in the same way that they speak of it in church. Nurses who blandly rush in to give a simple religious solution to the complex emotional problems of psychiatric patients need more insights into both religion and psychiatry.

Discussions about the Bible must also be related to the patient's condition. One patient asked a student nurse where in the Bible it told how many people were going to heaven and how many to hell when the end of time came. The nurse suggested that he read the book of Revelation. The patient made no effort to do so but continued to ask this nurse and others about the "signs" which would describe the end of the world. When the student mentioned this to her instructor, she was told that this patient was very anxious about his wife and his job. He feared that he was going to lose both, and his own personal world was on the brink of disaster. All of this caused him to be concerned about "the end." In the biblical passages about the end of the world he thought there might be found some answer to the coming catastrophes of his own personal world.

The nurse should not have referred him to the book of Revelation because the answer to the patient's problem will not be found in a book but in a new understanding of and confidence in himself. It is hoped that this will come to him through psychiatric interviews, pastoral counseling, the healing community of a hospital, and better family attitudes. Confidence is imparted to a psychiatric patient through personal relationships rather than through reading. The fear of people who have hurt him may be overcome by other people who love him.

Specific interpretation of such powerful spiritual medicine as the Bible offers should be given by chaplains, pastors, or doctors who are trained in its effects upon sick souls. Nurses also need to be cautious in the use of such religious words as "faith," "salvation," and "trust." These words must be related to specific human beings. Here is an example:

PATIENT: Oh, nurse, I feel so terrible. My stomach hurts, I shake inside, and my heart beats so fast.

NURSE: Mrs. X, you have improved since you have been here. These things take a little time before you feel completely well.

PATIENT: But nurse, I feel so sick. I'm not getting any better. I feel worse every day. (*Begins to cry.*) Oh, God help me!

NURSE: If you have faith, God *will* help you.

PATIENT: I hope so, nurse, and I *try* to have faith in him.

The patient has probably been trying to have "faith" for some time, but having faith is difficult in her present condition. Her relationships with other people are so mixed up that "faith" has become only a word. The nurse made the confusion worse with the assertion that God would help her if she had faith. The student was emphasizing an abstract term when she should have tried to communicate faith by her hope and encouragement. This patient did not need admonitions to have faith as much as she needed people who would be faithful to her.

Sometimes patients want to argue about religion. Although nurses are taught not to argue with patients, a nurse sometimes makes a mental exception of religion and attempts to "win" an argument, as in the following:

After having an argument with another patient concerning religion, Mr. A. approached a nurse with the statement:

MR. A.: I don't believe in any church's telling people what to do or how to live.

NURSE: A person should go to the Bible for guidance. Each church is striving to follow the teachings of the Scriptures. The church doesn't teach you how to live. The Bible does.

MR. A.: I know that, but some churches are always saying not to do this or it is wrong to do that.

NURSE: See what your Bible says, Mr. A., and compare it with what the church says. You will find out who is right.

MR. A.: My parents brought me up to believe in what the Baptist church teaches. I don't agree with all the things they teach.

NURSE: It is a parent's duty to rear his children in the knowledge of the Lord, and when they grow up, they must choose for themselves the way to go. If they have been reared to know God, then they will usually keep on knowing him.

The patient gained nothing from this discussion. In fact, it must have further irritated him. The nurse simply reiterated statements which she believed without considering the personal problems of this patient and the relationship of religion to them. The patient tried to talk about his problem with authority by expressing resentment against a church which tells a person what he ought to do or how he ought to live. But his complaint was smothered under the authoritarianism of the nurse. Finally, the patient who resented authority became more resistant inwardly and at the same time less confident of himself, of others, and of God. A more sensitive and less defensive nurse might have answered the patients first comment by saying, "Many people experience the same difficulty, Mr. A.," or, "Is this what the church meant to you?"

Nurses are also tempted to use reasoning which might be perfectly applicable to them but which is quite inconsistent with the condition of a patient. Nurses sometimes make suggestions about religion to psychiatric patients which are as magical as a suggestion that a man in a plaster cast should run a hundred yards.

Here is an interview which began with an interest in the patient but was marred by the nurse's attempt to get the patient to use religion as the nurse did. The patient tried to point out the fact that he was weak, but the nurse ignored it.

PATIENT: God doesn't care for me. No one does!
NURSE: Why do you say that?
PATIENT: My folks never come to see me or even write. I pray to God, and he does not listen.
NURSE: What makes you so sure he does not hear?
PATIENT: If he did, I would get better and be able to leave here.
NURSE: Don't you think you have to help yourself, too?
PATIENT: I am not capable of helping myself; I'm weak.
NURSE: Don't you think God can strengthen you, and then you'll be able to help yourself?
PATIENT: I guess so.

A more perceptive answer to the first question could have been an observation, "You feel all alone." The patient would then have been comforted by someone who understood what he felt.

Why is it difficult to relate religion to psychiatric problems? One difficulty is the assumption that religion is a magic which will heal all diseases and solve all personal problems without the patience, personal relationship, professional skill, and love which are part of the Christian heritage. Another problem is the lack of information concerning the relationship between religion and personality disorders. Sometimes a chaplain or a doctor can convey the understanding that is needed. Third, there is sometimes a lack of supervision and direction from the psychiatric staff concerning the personal dynamics of patients. The student nurse is left, therefore, to wander on her own in the midst of psychic pathology. She can hardly be blamed for using the few techniques she knows to meet problems that she poorly understands. The students whose examples were quoted above were trying in good faith to do the best they could. If someone had shown them the way, they might have better helped their patients. Of course, there are times when students are unable to see the limitations of religion even under the best of supervision. The nurse's ministry will be most effective when psychiatric and religious supervision are combined.

Finally, many people fail to see that Christianity is a religion of relationship between persons: God and man, man and man. In place of personal love between people, they see Christianity as a series of recipes for conduct or a system of clichés. Pastors, relatives, or staff people who hand out unreflective religious slogans like aspirin tablets may be shocked by patients' distortions of material or disillusioned because they do not change a sick person's basic attitudes. Words alone do not produce healing.

The Patient's Religious Concern

The attitude of the nurse toward religion and her outlook on life constitute one factor in psychiatric nursing. An equally important phase is the patient's own religious concern. In the brief space of one chapter only some of the ways in which religious concern is related to the psychoses can be discussed. An analysis was made by Wayne Oates of the religion of 68 patients at a state mental hospital in 1947. Another study was made, by the author, at Central State Hospital, Lakeland, Kentucky, of 173 first-admission patients from 1951 to 1953.[3] In the latter study the patients' religious concerns were analyzed as follows:

(1) In a few patients the psychosis was characterized by long-term moral and religious conflicts.

(2) In a few instances religion was a precipitating factor in a psychotic episode. For example, a fifty-year-old man stood up during a church service and told the pastor that he was going to preach about the sins of all the people in the congregation. When he was rejected by the church, he became violent and was hospitalized. His illness was related to deep feelings of guilt about adultery with a young woman and the inadequacy of his personal relationship with his wife. A church was the place in which the man sought to work out his moral problem.

---

[3] Wayne E. Oates, "The Role of Religion in the Psychoses," *Pastoral Psychology*, I (May, 1950), 35–40; and Samuel Southard, "Religious Concern in the Psychoses," *The Journal of Pastoral Care,* X (Winter, 1956), 226–33.

(3) There was a significant number of patients (13.6 per cent) who used religion to supply the words and phrases by which they talked about their problems. In about half of this number the religious ideas receded as the patient became quieter. One woman entered the hospital singing religious songs. After several days, when she was more in contact with reality, she was visited by the chaplain. She spoke of singing in her choir at home. She also worked with a Junior choir in which her own children participated. She did not remember singing when she entered the hospital. She sang with the other patients in chapel but was never boisterous on the ward again.

The other half of the patients who used religion to express their ideas were persons who often had a fixed delusion system. One patient consistently asked the chaplain how he knew voices came from God. Another patient repeated a story about a voice calling him to be a priest. A third was always asking about the unpardonable sin. These phrases have meaning for the patient. The work of the nurse, the doctor, and the chaplain is to make sense of the patient's problem.

One patient spoke of a revelation in which a voice told him that no woman was called to preach. He also wrote poems about Adam and Eve which revealed the wickedness of woman. In a series of pastoral interviews the patient began to speak of his problems with his wife, who had betrayed him on a number of occasions. He did not know how to win her back because he had always been a very passive person in his own home. He turned to religion for comfort and a rationalization of his own misery. In time he became well enough to admit to the chaplain that his visions were a comfort which he no longer needed because he was "doing God's work on the ward." This work was that of patient assistant to the night nurse. In this he found a healthier way of acting out his problems. Personal satisfaction in demonstrated performance gave him new stability. He was so effective and tender with other patients that the staff was somewhat reluctant to discharge him after several months of hospitalization.

(4) Some patients derived very positive benefits from their religion. This might occur even if they did not leave the hos-

pital. A grandmother who had recently been bereaved of her husband and two sons was brought to the hospital in a reactive depression. She felt very guilty about an attempted suicide during her depression. The nurses gave her much tender care and sympathy, and the doctor encouraged her to talk about her loss and give vent to her feelings. The chaplain helped her to resolve her guilt by looking upon the attempted suicide as a part of her illness. Within two months she was healed and back in her home, community and church.

Another patient found religion to be a comfort even though she could never leave the hospital. This was an elderly woman who was afraid that her daughter-in-law was going to poison her. She was never entirely relieved of the idea. Her son was unwilling for her to come back and live in his home. During her early days in the hospital she continually worried about her daughter-in-law and the "misery" she had caused. One day, as she was listening to the daily broadcast of religious music, she "felt that her burden was lifted." A hymn about casting burdens upon the Lord was being played. Probably the hymn in itself did not accomplish the healing, but it met at that particular moment the strivings which had been in the woman's heart for a number of weeks. There probably was some change in her self-evaluation prior to this incident. In any event, she later told her doctor that she was weary of carrying hate in her heart for her daughter-in-law and was willing for the Lord to take it all away. She remained too sick to go home but was a more contented patient and became a willing worker in the hospital.

(5) About 5 per cent of the patients raised issues which involved direct violation of community moral standards. These patients were conscious that their conduct had violated morality and were wrestling with a sense of responsibility for their actions. Their moral concerns were the central issue in their conversations with the chaplain.

All of these persons spoke of problems concerning either sex or hostility. Some of them could not remember what they had done but were sure that they "might have done something." These were not vague feelings of evil. The clinical records indicated the murder, incest, or adultery which plagued these suffering people.

(6) Over half the patients in both studies had no particular religious interest. In a few cases, as has been pointed out, they used religious phrases to describe their conflict. Mental patients will not get well by "getting religion," as is commonly conceived. But with a judicious combination of medical nursing and pastoral care, a significant number can be helped.

In the Central State Hospital study, about 12 per cent of the patients appeared to have a direct and positive benefit from their religion. This was possible only because patients were willing to accept their illness and the help of psychiatrists and nurses as well as that of the chaplain. There are some people who are genuinely afraid that psychiatry will take away their religion, and there are some who use this fear as an excuse for shunning treatment. Since these fears must be dealt with before either psychiatric or pastoral therapy is effective, some of the usual objections to psychiatric treatment that are found in some religious circles will be considered.

Common Religious Objections to Psychiatry

In *The Doctor's Profession* Daniel Jenkins has listed some of the widespread suspicions concerning psychiatrists.[4] Mr. Jenkins, a clergyman, compiled these ideas from the discussions of a group of Christian doctors who met regularly over a three-year period in England.

Some Christians are suspicious of psychiatrists because psychological theories that discard the necessity for the Christian revelation are sometimes used as philosophies of life. Although these theories are most directly stated by orthodox Freudian analysts, they seem to have been accepted by many laymen as the general view of psychiatrists. This attitude may result from the fact that many of the books on psychiatry read by laymen are written by Freudian analysts. Freud does leave the impression that he thought the religion of his day was an obsessive compulsive neu-

---

[4] London: Student Christian Movement Press, 1949, pp. 94–107.

rosis of social form.[5] However, a number of the working psychiatrists in the United States do not accept Freud's theories on religion.[6] Many psychiatrists are not only Christian in their attitudes and practice but also accept responsibilities in organized religion through various activities sponsored by churches.

Another suspicious attitude toward psychiatry is related to the philosophy of determinism, which seems to do away with personal responsibility. Sigmund Freud was a biological determinist who believed that men would be much more comfortable and moral if they would accept the basic biological drives which determine their personality structures. His early emphasis upon the predominantly sexual nature of these drives disturbed many religious people. These drives do condition human behavior, but they do not determine all that people do. Although theologians accept this opinion, there are also some competent psychologists, such as Dr. Gordon Allport of Harvard University, Dr. Rollo May, and Dr. Gardner Murphy of New York University, who stress the personal element in mature responsible conduct.[7]

This is a very tricky problem. On one hand, patients need to realize that they are not totally responsible for all their behavior. They must look at the conditioning influences of family, friends, and others. On the other hand, patients must be prevented from throwing all responsibility for their sickness upon others or on an early environment lest this become an excuse for a continuation of their sick way of life.

Some Christians are suspicious of psychiatry because they think it is an attempt to replace the work of the Catholic priest or the Protestant or Jewish counselor. Some people come to the hospital in a mood of religious defeat. They believe that if they could "just pray the matter through," they would not have to resort to psychiatrists. It is *either* religion *or* psychiatry to them.

---

[5] Sigmund Freud, "Obsessive Acts and Religious Practices," *Collected Papers* (London: Hogarth Press, 1949), II, 25–35.

[6] The most comprehensive study is *What Psychology Says About Religion* by Wayne E. Oates (New York: Association Press, 1958).

[7] Gordon Allport, *Becoming* (New Haven: University Press, 1955); Gardner Murphy, *Personality* (New York: Harper & Brothers, 1947); and Rollo May, *The Meaning of Anxiety* (New York: Ronald Press, 1950).

They do not see the interrelationship that was discussed on pages 194–98.

Other people draw back from psychiatry because popular writing gives exaggerated ideas of what psychotherapy can accomplish. These writings present a psychiatrist as a god. In certain instances a psychiatrist may appear to be almighty to a patient, either because the psychiatrist needs to feel omnipotent or because the patient is so weak that he must create a god whom he can worship in the flesh. But psychiatric textbooks are aware of this problem and make various suggestions concerning the way in which a psychiatrist can help a patient to reach a point in his personal development when he knows that the therapist is only human.

Finally, there are patients who shun a psychiatrist because they fear that their religion will be torn to pieces. If compulsive morality is being used as a defense, the psychiatrist will attempt to penetrate that defense in order that he may find the source of the patient's trouble. Psychiatrists are investigating motivation, which is a direct concern of religion. But what Freud called religion Christianity calls idolatry. The psychiatrist is doing Christianity a service when he helps a patient to see the difference between hollow piety and inner religious devotion.

On some occasions nurses may meet a psychiatrist who is openly contemptuous of religion. If he laughs scornfully at Judaism or Christianity in his psychotherapeutic interviews, he lacks professional competence. There are many excellent psychotherapists, like many other people, who have neglected their religion too long, but the problem with such doctors is that they are practicing inferior psychotherapy. A competent psychiatrist is respectful of the views of his patient and does not seek to impose his own spiritual judgments. This is a generally accepted professional commentary among psychiatrists themselves.

Some of the other therapeutic problems in relation to the religion of the mentally ill are discussed by Wayne Oates' *Religious Factors in Mental Illness*.[8] Nurses may also be interested in a

---

[8] New York: Association Press, 1955.

discussion of the question, "Is the Doctor a Christian?" in *The Family and Mental Illness*[9] by Samuel Southard, and in "Freud and Catholics," a pamphlet available from the America Press.[10]

When all these objections have been dealt with, there still is the question of spiritual values in psychiatry. Just what does religion do in psychiatric nursing?

Spiritual Values in Psychiatric Nursing

The *inner resources of the nurse and her attitudes toward people* was the first value of religion in nursing mentioned at the beginning of this chapter. There is a great deal of discouragement in the long-term care of psychiatric patients. Unless a nurse is continually renewed through an inner spring of faith and confidence in the purposes of God among men, she may succumb to cynicism, disillusionment, and the routine chipping away of her once-bright dreams. Some old patients can be so completely demoralized and some new patients so completely exasperating that it is difficult to remember that God has made man in his image. Therefore, it is important for the nurse to have her motivation renewed by the thought that Christ died for even the least of these.

This truth is referred to as an *inner* spring. It is not a club with which nurses are beaten into doing "religious duty." This attitude—that of duty—may cause interest in patients to die; part of the nurse will die, too. The nurse must admit her despair to God, humbly confess it to her colleagues, and let God and men help her where she actually is. No one senses hypocrisy quicker than a psychiatric patient, so the nurse might well take this golden opportunity to learn the value of honesty.

Another spiritual value in psychiatry is *fellowship*. From the time of the New Testament, Christians have been admonished to form a fellowship of suffering in order that no one may be isolated in his time of distress.[11] Nurses are working with men

---

[9] Philadelphia: Westminster Press, 1957, pp. 71–76.

[10] 70 E. 45th Street, New York 17, New York.

[11] 1 Peter 5:6–11; James 1:27; 5:13–20; Gal. 8:1–5; 1 Cor. 12:26; Heb. 10:32–39; Phil. 3:10.

and women whose disorganizing impulses have broken through their personal protections against such impulses. They must calm patients who fear that the "unspeakable things" in the depths of their souls may rush up and engulf them. The patient is judged to be sick, but at the same time, the healing community accepts him. The nurse is faced with the age-old Christian problem of communicating love and understanding to this patient at the same time that she refuses to blind herself to the limitations which are imposed by both his illness and her finitude.[12]

A third spiritual value is related to the sense of personal failure. The *pattern of reaction to personal failure* is as important as the failure itself. In psychiatric nursing a patient is complimented upon the way in which she handled a tantrum by calming down in the presence of a nurse whom she trusts. The patient may think that she failed because she began to shake inside and let her temper flare briefly. But the nurse may reassure her that she has progressed because she was only agitated momentarily and did not scream and kick as she had done previously.

When individuals react to personal failure by concealment, compromise, diversion, bluffing, shifting of responsibility, withdrawal, or surrender, they are headed for trouble. But if they can *confront each problem openly*, personal failure may become a precondition of growth. Frank recognition and intelligent handling may lead to better social adjustment and a spiritual singleness of heart. Concealment or surrender may lead to the forms of mental illness which are described under such terms as "paranoid" and "hebephrenic." The personality changes and upheavals arising out of the sense of personal failure have been described by Anton Boisen in *Religion in Crisis and Custom.*[13]

---

[12] Gal. 6:1.

[13] New York: Harper & Brothers, 1955, pp. 41–70.

14. Nursing as a Christian Vocation

SINCE THE FOUNDATION of the profession nursing has been regarded as a Christian calling. Jamieson and Sewall traced the origin of the nursing profession to the early Christian orders of deacons and deaconesses.[1] In modern history the order of deaconesses among the Mennonites in Holland so impressed a Lutheran, Pastor Fliedner, that he decided to begin a similar order in his own church. Three kinds of deaconesses were to be educated: the first group to care for the sick, the poor, and unmarried pregnant girls; the second group to teach; and the third group to do parish work.[2] The work was established in a large home in Kaiserwerth, Germany. About 1845 Pastor Fliedner began to train young women in nursing, and the idea grew of consecrated women devoting their lives to a healing ministry. When Florence Nightingale decided to become a Christian lay nurse, she traveled to Kaiserwerth for some of her training. It was here that she found an expression of her ideals.[3]

There are three doctrines in the New Testament which relate to a person's profession or calling. The first of these is the call to lead a life worthy of a Christian. Those who have accepted salvation in Jesus Christ are challenged to be blameless in the

[1] *Trends in Nursing History* (Philadelphia: W. B. Saunders, 1941), pp. 105–7.

[2] Scherzer, *The Church and Healing* (Philadelphia: Westminster Press, 1950), p. 117.

[3] *Ibid.*, p. 118.

church, the community, and the family and at work.[4] Peter proclaimed that Christians were "a royal priesthood."[5] Each believer is a "priest," a minister to his brother in need.

The responsibility to lead a worthy life is upon every person who obeys God's call to a new way of life. The same ethical living is expected of Christians in medicine, nursing, the ministry, business, or custodial services. The nurse should not think of herself as someone on a higher ethical plane than a secretary; the requirements of moral living are basically the same in all professions or services.

Second, Christian theology recognizes a variety of services within which a person may use the gifts or talents God has bestowed on him. No one profession has more honor before God than another.[6] Martin Luther wrote: "All works, let their name be what it may, become great only when they flow from faith, the first, greatest, and noblest of works."[7] The nurse who uses her talents faithfully is serving God as much as the priest or minister.

Third, those who are called of God are to give evidence through their living of their particular calling. The New Testament contained requirements for those who would be bishops or deacons.[8] Similarly, a nurse or a person in any other profession must submit to supervision and observation before the community will approve their service.

The Worthiness of Daily Work

The quality of daily work is a measure of spiritual devotion. There are certain attitudes which will improve the effectiveness of a nurse's ministry.[9]

One of the required attitudes is objectivity. The nurse who is guided by her own private wishes will act like an amateur rather than as a professionally trained person. A professional person does his work well whether he feels good or not. He is objec-

---

[4] Eph. 4–6.
[5] 1 Peter 2:9.
[6] 1 Cor. 12:1–30.
[7] *Op. cit.*, I, 179.
[8] 1 Tim. 3:1–7; 2 Tim. 2:20–26; Titus 1:5–9.
[9] These are adapted from *God and the Day's Work* by Robert Calhoun (New York: Association Press, 1943).

tive; that is, he has a measure of self-forgetfulness and devotion to his task which transcends his personal likes and dislikes. He shares common concerns with other persons who have similar training. Mutual trust and confidence characterize his professional relationships.

Persistent, keen effort is another measure of spiritual devotion in nursing. The medieval church counted sloth, or apathy, as one of the seven deadly sins. Under the pressure of many duties a nurse is often tempted to "cut corners" in her work. She may become less exacting in her studies. Sheer fatigue must be fought.

The answer to this strenuous life is to be found in steady, purposeful activity. An ordered pattern of study and an alert attitude on duty are aspects of Christian service.

Lastly, there must be the attitude of an eager learner. The nurse who is religiously alert will be wide awake as she approaches new phases of her chosen profession. Each subject brings her closer to the fulfilment of her desire to serve God and man as a nurse. This fresh vigor is necessary as the mind staggers under an accumulation of textbook facts or classroom instruction. Devotion to a great cause will bring a daily renewal of intellectual and emotional vigor.

The Sense of Commitment

At the heart of a Christian profession is the inner resolve to walk worthily in the way of God's call. This requires a sense of identification of self with those who live for a great purpose. The student should see in some godly person the qualities of Christ which she desires to incorporate into her own life.

In nursing, a sense of commitment leads one to take people seriously because they are created in the image of God. A nurse must fight "institutionalization" both in herself and in her patients. When she is committed to her service, she may see the same problems time and again, but people do not become monotonous to her. She finds the image of God uniquely in each person.

Christian commitment is communicated by attitudes, gestures, and intonation as well as by words. The student can observe this in those men and women who exemplify the best and who bear their profession with dignity and humility.

In the midst of many requirements there is a religious question: What does the Lord require of you? The prophet Micah proclaimed this answer to God's call:

> He has showed you, O man, what is good;
> and what does the Lord require of you
> but to do justice, and to love kindness,
> and to walk humbly with your God? [10]

[10] Mic. 6:8.

Index